The Open University

Universal processes

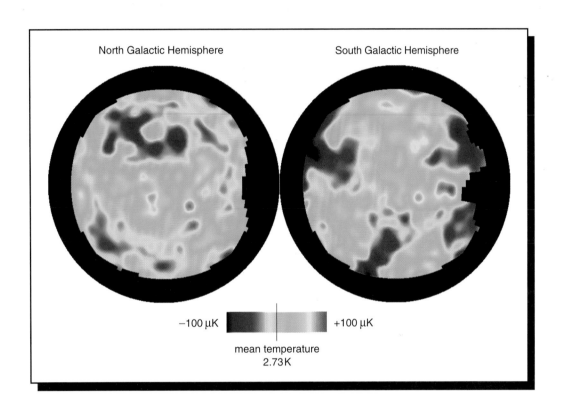

North Galactic Hemisphere   South Galactic Hemisphere

−100 μK   +100 μK

mean temperature
2.73K

11

Picture on title page This colour-coded map shows departures from uniformity in the cosmic microwave background radiation over the whole sky. The two panels correspond to two 'halves' of the sky, projected onto a flat picture. The scale represents the temperature either side of the mean temperature of 2.73 K. Violet regions are slightly cooler than the mean value of 2.73 K, red regions are slightly hotter, by about 100 microkelvin (μK). Most of the variations seen are believed to represent localized variations in the density of matter at a time 300 000 years after the Big Bang, when this radiation interacted with matter for the last time. This map is the final result after four years operation of the COBE satellite.

The Open University, Walton Hall, Milton Keynes MK7 6AA

First published 1998

Written, edited, designed and typeset by the Open University.

Printed and bound in the United Kingdom by Jarrold Book Printing, Norfolk, England.

ISBN 0 7492 8197 9

This text forms part of an Open University course, S103 *Discovering Science*. The complete list of texts that make up this course can be found on the back cover. Details of this and other Open University courses can be obtained from the Course Reservations and Sales Office, PO Box 724, The Open University, Milton Keynes MK7 6ZS, United Kingdom: tel. (00 44) 1908 653231.

For availability of this or other course components, contact Open University Worldwide Ltd, The Berrill Building, Walton Hall, Milton Keynes MK7 6AA, United Kingdom: tel. (00 44) 1908 858585, fax (00 44) 1908 858787, e-mail ouwenq@open.ac.uk. Alternatively, much useful course information can be obtained from the Open University's website http://www.open.ac.uk

s103block11i1.1

Contents

Introduction

1

In Block 10 you saw how the age of the Earth can be measured and how events in its past history can be studied by looking at the record laid down in the Earth's rocks. In this block we widen the scope of the course in both time and space to investigate the age and history of the Universe as a whole. Some of the questions we will be answering in Block 11 are: How and when did the Universe begin? How has it evolved since then? What are the fundamental interactions that govern its behaviour? What will happen to the Universe in the future?

Answers to questions like these are the subjects of particle physics and cosmology. Scientists who work in these two apparently unrelated areas of science — one concerned with the unimaginably small, the other with the infinitely large — have in recent years come together in an attempt to understand the Universe. Cosmology is the branch of science that involves the study of the Universe as a whole. The research tools of cosmologists are powerful telescopes, such as those in Figure 1.1, which are able to detect galaxies out to the furthest reaches of the Universe. You will get a flavour of this work when you use a 'virtual telescope' later in the block to measure the expansion rate of the Universe, and so calculate its age. It may seem strange that people working in this field should count particle physicists amongst their closest allies. As you saw in Block 7, the research tools of the particle physicists are the giant particle accelerators, such as that shown in Figure 1.2, in which high-energy beams of particles are smashed together, enabling details of exotic reactions to be investigated and understood. But this is the key to the union of these two subjects. For only in particle accelerators are scientists able to recreate the high-energy conditions that once existed in the Universe during the first moments of its creation. When particle physicists study these reactions they can provide cosmologists with a window on the Universe when it was only one-thousandth of a billionth of a second old.

Figure 1.1 The twin domes of the W. M. Keck Observatory, 4 200 m above sea-level on the summit of Mauna Kea, Hawaii. These huge domes each house a telescope whose primary mirror is 10 m in diameter. When they were completed in 1997 these telescopes were the largest in the world, enabling astronomers to observe objects up to 250 million times fainter, and see detail on a scale 500 times finer, than can be seen with the naked eye.

Figure 1.2 The Large Hadron Collider (LHC) at CERN, the European Laboratory for Particle Physics near Geneva in Switzerland. The LHC consists of a ring 27 km in circumference, within which two high-energy beams of protons will collide head-on, with an energy of over 10^{13} eV. When completed in 2005 it will enable particle physicists to recreate conditions that existed only 10^{-12} s after the Big Bang, that is thought to mark the creation of the Universe.

An example of the interplay between these two areas of study concerns the fundamental particles known as neutrinos, which you read about in Block 7 (see the table of particles on the Study Guide for Block 11). A few years ago, cosmologists announced that there can be no more than three flavours of neutrino. If there were four, say, then they calculated that there would be more helium in the Universe than is actually observed, as a result of particle reactions that occurred in the early Universe. Particle physicists, studying decays of exotic particles in their high-energy accelerators, were also able to calculate how many types of neutrino there are in the Universe. The answer the particle physicists arrived at was also three — if there were more, or less, flavours of neutrinos, the particles under study would have decayed at a different rate. So we can be sure that there really are only three types of neutrino in the Universe — whether the problem is tackled from the large or the small scale.

The important idea here is that particle physics and cosmology complement each other. They are two research areas at the forefront of scientific understanding, and we hope you will find learning about them to be both stimulating and rewarding. Some of the ideas discussed in this block may challenge the view of the world that you currently hold, and throughout history such challenges have been one of the hallmarks of scientific progress. Apart from the intellectual excitement of these topics, they serve to illustrate the way in which scientists continually strive to push back the boundaries of knowledge, extrapolating from what can be measured in the laboratory to realms that are impossible to study directly.

In Sections 2 and 3 we'll be concerned with the overall structure and composition of the Universe (a topic you met briefly in Block 3) and, more specifically, with how the structure and composition have changed throughout time. As you'll see, the Universe is not static — it was different in the past to how it is now, and it will be different again in the future. Our understanding of this evolution relies crucially on two pieces of evidence: first, evidence that the Universe is *expanding* and, second, evidence that the Universe is *cooling*.

Any attempt to chart the history of our evolving Universe must take account of the laws that are believed to govern all physical processes. Accordingly, in Sections 4 to 9, there are accounts of the distinctive features of the four types of interaction of all matter and radiation: electromagnetic, strong, weak and gravitational. Next, in Section 10, the question is raised as to whether these four interactions are truly distinct. Might there be bigger and better theories, unifying two or more of the four interactions.

Bringing together the information from the rest of the block, the last two sections (Sections 11 and 12) present a history of the Universe, from the earliest times of which one can meaningfully speak, through the present day, and into the distant future.

Question 1.1   To revise what you learned about the contents of the Universe in Block 3, place the following terms in hierarchical order from smallest to largest, and explain briefly what is meant by each: cluster of galaxies, planet, galaxy, star. ◄

Activity 1.1   Revision: light and spectra

This activity allows you to revise some of the material from Block 7 in order to prepare yourself for the first part of Block 11. ◄

Activity 1.2   Revision: powers of ten

This activity allows you to revise your understanding of powers of ten. You will need to be comfortable with calculations involving powers of ten throughout this block. ◄

2 The expanding Universe

The deduction that the Universe is expanding is based on measurements of two quantities for each of thousands of galaxies: their distance away from us and the speed with which they are moving. Each of these quantities is determined in a quite straightforward manner by applying laws of physics that you have already met — but applying them to situations on a much larger scale of both distance and time than anything you have so far come across in this course.

In order to make any sense of the observations that will be discussed, it is necessary to assume that the laws of physics that operate in distant parts of the Universe (distant in both time and space) are the same as those that operate in laboratories on the Earth. In fact, this is only an extreme version of an assumption that underlies the whole of science: we assume that the laws of physics were the same in Birmingham yesterday as they will be in Bangalore tomorrow, for instance. If this were not true, then no further progress would be possible. Conversely, the fact that apparently sensible conclusions can be reached by making just this one assumption, tends to indicate that it is not such a bad assumption after all. If such assumptions were to lead to inconsistencies with observations, then we would have to re-examine the original assumptions and possibly modify the laws of physics as they are currently expressed. This process is the essence of the *scientific method* that you have met many times throughout this course.

○ When trying to discover the properties of a distant galaxy, what is the *only* thing that astronomers can actually measure that comes from the galaxy in question?

○ The *only* thing that can be measured is the *light* (or other electromagnetic radiation) emitted by the galaxy. So the only knowledge astronomers can have about a distant galaxy comes from measurements of this radiation. (In the future it may also be possible to measure *gravitational radiation* too, as you will see in Section 8.)

When the light from a galaxy is collected using telescopes, different types of measurements can be made on it. The simplest measurement is to determine how *bright* the galaxy appears to be, that is how much light emitted by the galaxy is detected here on Earth. A slightly more complex measurement is to look at how that light is distributed with wavelength, that is to examine the *spectrum* of light emitted by the galaxy. As you will see in the rest of this section, it is measurements of the brightness and the spectrum of a distant galaxy that can lead to determinations of its distance and speed, respectively.

2.1 Measuring the distance to galaxies

The unit of length used when measuring the distance to galaxies is discussed in Box 2.1, *Astronomical distance units*, which you should read before proceeding with this section.

Box 2.1 *Astronomical distance units*

Astronomical distances are so enormous that metres (or even kilometres) are too small a unit to be convenient when measuring them. For this reason cosmologists usually use a different unit known as the *parsec*. The definition of this unit of distance relies on the phenomenon of *parallax*, which is discussed below.

As the Earth orbits the Sun, so the apparent positions of nearby stars shift, by tiny amounts, with respect to more distant background stars. You can see the same effect by holding your index finger up in front of your face and looking at it alternately with (only) your left eye and then (only) your right eye. Your finger will appear to shift with respect to more distant objects. Try it now!

By taking photographs of the same part of the sky, six months apart, nearby stars will be seen to exhibit very small shifts from one photograph to the next. This phenomenon is referred to as *parallax*. As shown in Figure 2.1, the parallax can be quantified by the angle ψ (the Greek letter *psi*, pronounced 'p-sigh'). The **parallax angle** is defined as *half* the angular shift of the star, as measured from two positions in the Earth's orbit, six months apart.

So, by measuring the parallax angle of a nearby star, we can calculate its distance using simple trigonometry on the right-angled triangle shown in Figure 2.1. Recall from Block 7 Box 8.2, that if the angle ψ and the length of the side opposite the angle are known, the tangent of the angle can be used to find the length r. The tangent of an angle is the length of the side of the triangle opposite the angle, divided by the length of the side adjacent to the angle. In this case we have:

$$\tan \psi = \frac{\text{opp}}{\text{adj}} = \frac{1.5 \times 10^{11} \, \text{m}}{r} \qquad (2.1)$$

A distance of one **parsec** is defined to be that distance at which a star would exhibit a parallax angle of one arc second (i.e. $\psi = \frac{1}{3\,600}$ of a degree, as there are 60 arc minutes in a degree and 60 arc seconds in an arc minute). In fact the word 'parsec' is simply an abbreviation of 'parallax arc second'. Substituting these numbers into Equation 2.1, we have:

$$\tan \left(\frac{1}{3\,600} \right)^{\circ} = \frac{1.5 \times 10^{11} \, \text{m}}{1 \, \text{pc}}$$

This may be rearranged to calculate the size of one parsec:

$$1 \, \text{pc} = \frac{1.5 \times 10^{11} \, \text{m}}{\tan (1/3\,600)^{\circ}} = \frac{1.5 \times 10^{11} \, \text{m}}{4.8 \times 10^{-6}} = 3.1 \times 10^{16} \, \text{m}$$

So, one parsec (1 pc) is equal to about 3×10^{16} m.

In fact, no stars are as close as 1 pc; the nearest star to the Earth, Proxima Centauri, is about 1.3 pc away, and has a parallax angle of just 0.75 arc seconds. For small angles such as this, $r = \dfrac{1}{\psi}$ when ψ is measured in arc seconds and r is measured in parsecs. Parallax angles as small as 10^{-3} of an arc second can now be measured. This means that distances can be measured directly for stars that are situated up to 1 000 pc away.

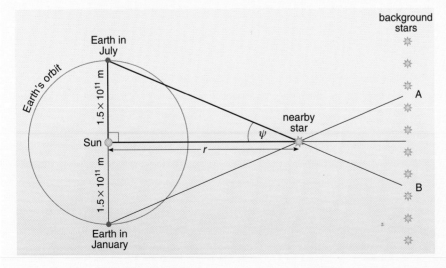

Figure 2.1 An illustration of parallax. The position of a hypothetical nearby star, situated a distance r away, exhibits a tiny angular shift when viewed from the Earth at two intervals. The nearby star appears at location A in January and at location B in July. The parallax angle ψ is defined as half the angular shift between two such positions, six months apart. As noted in Block 3, the mean distance of the Earth from the Sun is about 1.5×10^{11} m. (Note, this diagram is not to scale.)

For stars more distant than this, other methods to determine their distance must be used. Notice that, since the distances to stars are so much greater than the distance between the Earth and Sun, it makes no difference whether we measure the distance to a star from the Sun or from the Earth. The answer is the same.

Having defined the parsec to be a distance of about 3×10^{16} m, we no longer need to worry about parallax and trigonometry, but can simply use the parsec as a convenient unit of distance. As illustrated in Figure 2.2, our own galaxy, the Milky Way, is about 4×10^4 pc, or 40 kpc (40 kiloparsecs), in diameter and one of our nearest neighbours, the Andromeda Galaxy (Block 5, Figure 2.3), is about 6.6×10^5 pc or 660 kpc (660 kiloparsecs) distant from us. Clusters of galaxies typically lie at distances of several hundred million parsecs away (one million parsecs, 10^6 pc, is written as 1 Mpc or 1 megaparsec), or even several billion parsecs away (one billion parsecs, 10^9 pc, is written as 1 Gpc or 1 gigaparsec).

Question 2.1 A cluster of galaxies is said to be at a distance of 200 Mpc from the Earth. What is this distance in metres? ◀

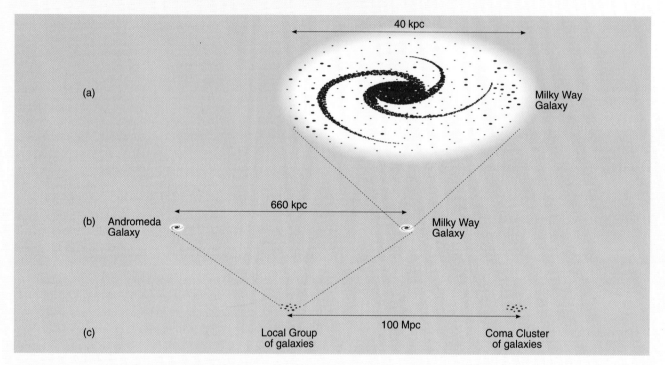

Figure 2.2 A schematic representation of distance scales in the Universe. (a) Our own galaxy, the Milky Way, is about 40 kpc in diameter. (b) The distance from our own galaxy to the Andromeda Galaxy is about 660 kpc, which is around 16 times the diameter of the Milky Way. (c) Our own galaxy and the Andromeda Galaxy are both part of the so-called Local Group of galaxies. The distance from the Local Group to the Coma Cluster of galaxies is about 100 Mpc, which means that the Coma Cluster is around 150 times further away from us than is the Andromeda Galaxy.

An important method by which distances to galaxies are determined is based on a simple relationship between the **luminosity** of a galaxy (the total power it emits, measured in watts) and the **brightness** of the galaxy as seen at the Earth (the power received per unit area, measured in watts per square metre). To appreciate this relationship, consider the following thought experiment.

○ Imagine that you have two identical torches — both have the same luminosity and so they emit the same power. You switch them on, then place one of them 100 m away from you, and the other only 20 m away. In the dark, how can you tell which of the two torches is nearer to you?

The nearer torch will appear to be brighter than the one that is more distant. So, even though the two torches have the same luminosity, they have different brightnesses because they are at different distances away from you.

In order to see the relationship between the luminosity and brightness of an object, look at the situation depicted in Figure 2.3. This shows two galaxies labelled A and B, which have the same luminosity, but are at different distances from the Earth. As the light from each galaxy travels out into space, so the light spreads out over the surfaces of imaginary spheres, centred on the galaxy. By the time it reaches the Earth, the light from the more distant galaxy is spread out over a larger sphere than the light from the nearer galaxy. So the more distant galaxy will appear less bright than the nearby galaxy.

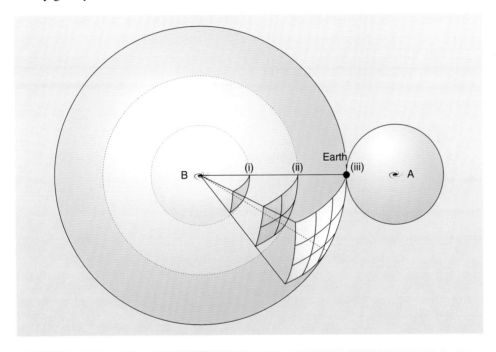

Figure 2.3 The light from distant galaxies spreads out over the surfaces of imaginary spheres centred on each galaxy. Galaxies A and B have the same luminosity but are situated at different distances from the Earth. For galaxy B, three spherical surfaces are shown at regularly increasing distances away from the galaxy. The light that reaches (i) becomes spread out over four times the area by the time it reaches (ii) and over nine times the area at (iii), by the time it reaches the Earth. Consequently, galaxy B would appear nine time less bright to an observer at (iii) than it would to an observer at (i). Galaxy A is closer than galaxy B, its light is spread out over a smaller sphere by the time it reaches the Earth, and so it appears brighter.

At a distance r away from a galaxy, the brightness (measured in watts per square metre) will be equal to the luminosity L (measured in watts) of the galaxy divided by the surface area of a sphere of radius r.

In order to quantify this relationship, some ideas about measuring spheres are needed. You should therefore read through Box 2.2, *Circles and spheres*, before proceeding.

Box 2.2 *Circles and spheres*

It has been known since ancient times that for *any* circle, the ratio of its circumference to its diameter is a constant value. This constant is given the symbol π (the Greek letter *pi*, pronounced 'pie') and is equal to 3.141 592 654 (to nine decimal places). The value should be stored on your calculator — look for the π button (or refer to the manual).

$$\frac{\text{circumference of a circle}}{\text{diameter of a circle}} = \pi$$

It is often more convenient to work with the radius of a circle rather than its diameter, and since the radius r is half the diameter, the length of the circumference of any circle is:

circumference of a circle = $2\pi r$

The area of any circle is also related to its radius and the constant π. Although the proof of this need not concern us here, the area of any circle is given by the formula:

area of a circle = πr^2

A sphere can be thought of as a three-dimensional circle, and as you might expect, the surface area and volume of a sphere also depend on the sphere's radius and the constant π. Again, proofs of the following formulae need not concern us here, and we merely state that:

surface area of a sphere = $4\pi r^2$

and

volume of a sphere = $\frac{4}{3}\pi r^3$

Question 2.2 In order to check that you can apply these formulae correctly, and use the π button on your calculator, try the following calculations.

(a) What are the circumference and the area of a circle whose radius is 5.00 cm?

(b) What are the surface area and the volume of a sphere whose radius is also 5.00 cm? ◄

The brightness of an object is sometimes called the 'flux' of light and so is usually represented by the symbol F. Since the surface area of a sphere of radius r is given by $4\pi r^2$, the brightness F of an object may be *defined* as:

$$F = \frac{L}{4\pi r^2} \tag{2.2}$$

As we have already said, when observing a distant galaxy, all that cosmologists can measure is its brightness F. But if the luminosity L of the galaxy is known, then the distance r to it can be calculated, using Equation 2.2.

If galaxy A in Figure 2.3 has a luminosity L of 1×10^{41} W, and its brightness F is measured as 9×10^{-10} W m^{-2}, how far away is the galaxy?

First, Equation 2.2 must be rearranged to make r the subject:

$$r^2 = \frac{L}{4\pi F}$$

Then, taking the square root of both sides,

$$r = \sqrt{\frac{L}{4\pi F}}$$

So in this case,

$$r = \sqrt{\frac{1 \times 10^{41}\,\text{W}}{4\pi \times 9 \times 10^{-10}\,\text{W m}^{-2}}} = \sqrt{9 \times 10^{48}\,\text{m}^2} = 3 \times 10^{24}\,\text{m}$$

Since 1 pc is equal to about $3 \times 10^{16}\,\text{m}$ (see Box 2.1),

$$r = \frac{3 \times 10^{24}}{3 \times 10^{16}}\,\text{pc} = 10^8\,\text{pc, or } 100\,\text{Mpc}$$

But how do we determine the luminosity of the galaxy in the first place? In practice this is based on the following statistical argument. Clusters of galaxies can contain anything from a few dozen to a few thousand individual galaxies. When cosmologists look at a cluster, such as the Coma Cluster of galaxies shown in Figure 2.4, they see that all the galaxies within it have different brightnesses. Now, on the scale of the Universe it is usually adequate to assume that all galaxies in a single cluster are at about the same distance from us. (The distances between individual galaxies in a cluster — a few hundred kiloparsecs — are small when compared with the distance of the cluster from us — usually hundreds of megaparsecs, Figure 2.2.) So the variation in brightness of galaxies within a cluster must reflect an intrinsic variation in luminosity from one member galaxy to the next. The assumption that cosmologists make is that, wherever they find reasonably large clusters (say more than a hundred members), the *tenth brightest* galaxy in any one cluster has roughly the same luminosity as the tenth brightest galaxy in any other cluster. The tenth brightest is therefore assumed to be a typical galaxy for any cluster.

Activity 2.1 *Finding the typical member of a sample*
To appreciate this statistical argument, try this short practical activity. ◀

Figure 2.4   An image of the Coma Cluster of galaxies, covering an area of sky about one-quarter the size of the full Moon. This cluster of galaxies is situated at about 100 Mpc away, and individual members have a range of different brightnesses. In fact, virtually all of the objects in this image are galaxies in the cluster. An exception is the bright object at the top, centre, which is a foreground star within our own galaxy. (The 'spikes' are an artefact caused by the camera.)

Measurements of nearby clusters of galaxies, whose distances can be estimated by more direct methods, indicate that the assumption of the tenth brightest galaxies all having roughly the same luminosity is valid, and the value of this luminosity is about $L_{10} = 1 \times 10^{41}\,\text{W}$. Therefore we can assume that the luminosity of the tenth brightest galaxy in *any* cluster is $L_{10} = 1 \times 10^{41}\,\text{W}$, and so the distance to *any* cluster can be found by measuring the brightness of its tenth brightest member, F_{10}. As you saw earlier, Equation 2.2 can be rearranged to make r the subject, so in this case:

$$r = \sqrt{\frac{L_{10}}{4\pi F_{10}}} \tag{2.3}$$

In practice, the procedure for determining the distance to a cluster is often based on *comparing* the brightnesses of a pair of galaxies in different clusters, which are assumed to have the same luminosity (both are tenth brightest), and where the distance to one of them is already known. Equation 2.2 can be written as $L = 4\pi r^2 F$. So, if two galaxies A and B have the same luminosity, i.e. we can say $L_A = L_B$, then their brightnesses, F_A and F_B, and their distances, r_A and r_B will be related by:

$$4\pi r_A^2 F_A = 4\pi r_B^2 F_B$$

If we divide both sides of the equation by 4π, it can be simplified to give:

$$r_A^2 F_A = r_B^2 F_B$$

Finally, this may be rearranged to give:

$$\frac{r_A^2}{r_B^2} = \frac{F_B}{F_A} \tag{2.4}$$

The following question shows how this equation can be used.

Suppose that Figure 2.3 shows the tenth brightest galaxies, labelled A and B, in a couple of clusters. If galaxy A has a measured brightness of 9×10^{-10} W m^{-2} and is situated 100 Mpc away, and galaxy B has a measured brightness of 1×10^{-10} W m^{-2}, what is the distance to the cluster in which galaxy B sits?

First we rearrange Equation 2.4 to make r_B the subject:

$$r_B^2 = r_A^2 \frac{F_A}{F_B}$$

so $r_B = \sqrt{r_A^2 \frac{F_A}{F_B}}$

Substituting the values above, we find:

$$r_B = \sqrt{(100\,\text{Mpc})^2 \times \left(\frac{9 \times 10^{-10}\,\text{W m}^{-2}}{1 \times 10^{-10}\,\text{W m}^{-2}}\right)}$$

$$= \sqrt{(100\,\text{Mpc})^2 \times 9} \quad = 300\,\text{Mpc}$$

So galaxy B is three times further away than galaxy A and, by implication, the cluster of galaxies in which galaxy B sits is three times further away than the cluster of galaxies containing galaxy A.

Alternatively, you could simply note that galaxy B is nine times fainter than galaxy A, so its light must be spread out over the surface of a sphere which has nine times greater area than that for galaxy A (as shown in Figure 2.3). The surface area of a sphere depends on its radius squared or, turning this around, the distance depends on the square root of the surface area of the sphere. So galaxy B must be $\sqrt{9} = 3$ times further away than galaxy A.

Question 2.3   (a) If galaxy A appeared to be 25 times brighter than galaxy B, how would their distances compare?

(b) If galaxy B were six times further away than galaxy A, how would their brightnesses compare? ◀

Question 2.4   The tenth brightest galaxy of the cluster in the constellation of Perseus has a measured brightness of 1.0×10^{-9} W m^{-2} and is at a distance of 91 Mpc from the Earth. The tenth brightest galaxy of the cluster in the constellation of Corona Borealis has a measured brightness of 7.2×10^{-11} W m^{-2}. What is the distance from the Earth to the cluster in Corona Borealis? ◀

2.2   Measuring the speed of galaxies

We now consider how to measure the speed with which a galaxy is moving away from (or towards) us. Once again this is based on measurements made on the light emitted by a galaxy, but this time we need to examine the spectrum of light — how it is distributed with wavelength — rather than the total amount of light emitted. It may not be immediately obvious what spectra have to do with speed measurements, but this will soon become apparent.

You saw in Block 7 that the wavelength of spectral lines from an energy saver light bulb can be measured using a diffraction grating. The principle of measuring spectral lines in the light from a star or galaxy is exactly the same. A telescope is pointed at the object in question and its spectrum is obtained by using a grating to diffract the light which is detected. The spectrum is recorded using an electronic imaging device, similar to that in a home video camera, and the information is stored on a computer for processing.

As you saw in Block 7, there are two ways of representing such a spectrum. First, a spectrum can be displayed as an image of one order from the diffraction pattern. Figure 2.5a shows such an image of a spectrum from a typical star. The intensity of the light at any point in the spectrum is represented by the grey scale of the image at that point — darker grey indicates lower intensity. Second, the spectrum may be displayed as a graph, known as a spectral distribution, as shown in Figure 2.5b. This is the same spectrum as in Figure 2.5a, just displayed in the alternative representation.

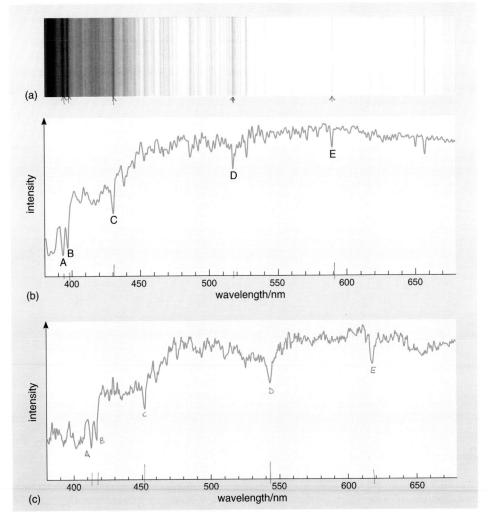

Figure 2.5 (a) and (b) show two representations of the spectrum of a star. Here, violet light is displayed towards the left of the spectrum ($\lambda = 380$ nm) and red light to the right ($\lambda = 680$ nm). Note that the order of the colours in the spectrum is reversed compared with the spectra displayed in Block 7, because there we plotted spectra against photon energy, and $E_{ph} \propto 1/\lambda$. (a) An image of one order from the diffraction pattern. (b) The spectral distribution of the same spectrum. Absorption lines are visible as dark bands in (a) and as dips in the graph in (b). (c) A spectrum of a distant galaxy shown in the same representation as (b).

⬤ In the practical activity in Block 7 (Activity 10.1) you examined the spectra of both a tungsten filament light bulb and an energy saver light bulb. What were the features of these spectra?

◯ The tungsten filament light bulb produced a continuous spectrum, emitting light of all colours with a smooth distribution. The energy saver light bulb produced an emission spectrum in which bright coloured lines were seen at specific wavelengths.

The spectrum of a star clearly differs from the spectrum of either of the bulbs that you examined in Block 7. The spectrum of a typical star may be described as showing an absorption spectrum in which *dark* lines are superimposed on a *bright* background. You saw in Block 7 how absorption spectra are produced when light with a continuous spectrum passes through gas that absorbs light of only specific energies. The bright, continuous, background in the spectrum from a star is produced by photons coming from deep in its atmosphere. As these photons emerge through the star's cooler, outermost layers, photons with certain energies are absorbed by atoms. The absorption lines are therefore characteristic of the particular elements that are present in the outermost layers of the star.

When the spectra of distant galaxies are examined, similar absorption line spectra are seen to those of stars in our own galaxy. An example of a galaxy spectrum is shown in Figure 2.5c, where it may be compared with the spectrum of the typical star in Figure 2.5b. It is not surprising that the two spectra are rather similar, since the spectrum of the galaxy is simply the sum of the spectra of the billions of stars that comprise it. Because most galaxies are far away, telescopes are unable to distinguish individual stars within them.

⬤ Five of the strongest absorption lines in the spectrum of the star are labelled A–E in Figure 2.5b. Can you identify this same pattern of lines in the spectrum of the galaxy (Figure 2.5c)? What do you notice about the positions of the lines in the galaxy spectrum, relative to their positions in the star spectrum?

◯ The same basic *pattern* of absorption lines appears in each spectrum, but the *positions* of the lines are different. In particular, the lines in the spectrum of the galaxy (Figure 2.5c) are displaced to longer wavelengths, relative to those in the star (Figure 2.5b). For example, absorption line C appears at about 430 nm in Figure 2.5b but at about 450 nm in Figure 2.5c.

It is assumed that the absorption lines seen in the spectrum of the distant galaxy are due to the *same* atomic transitions in the *same* elements as those seen in the spectra of the Sun and other stars within our own galaxy. The difference is that the absorption lines in the spectrum of the distant galaxy are shifted towards longer wavelengths.

Shifted wavelengths have a very natural interpretation in everyday life. The phenomenon is known as the **Doppler effect** and it is probably familiar to you in the context of sound waves, although it applies equally to any wave motion, including electromagnetic radiation such as light. The Doppler effect with sound is perhaps most noticeable when an approaching ambulance sounds its siren or as a speeding car races past. As the vehicle approaches and then recedes, apart from growing louder and then fainter, the pitch of the sound is perceived as higher when the vehicle is approaching than when it is receding. As shown in Figure 2.6, this can be understood in terms of the sound waves getting 'bunched up' in front of the vehicle as it approaches, and 'stretched out' behind the vehicle as it recedes. This happens simply

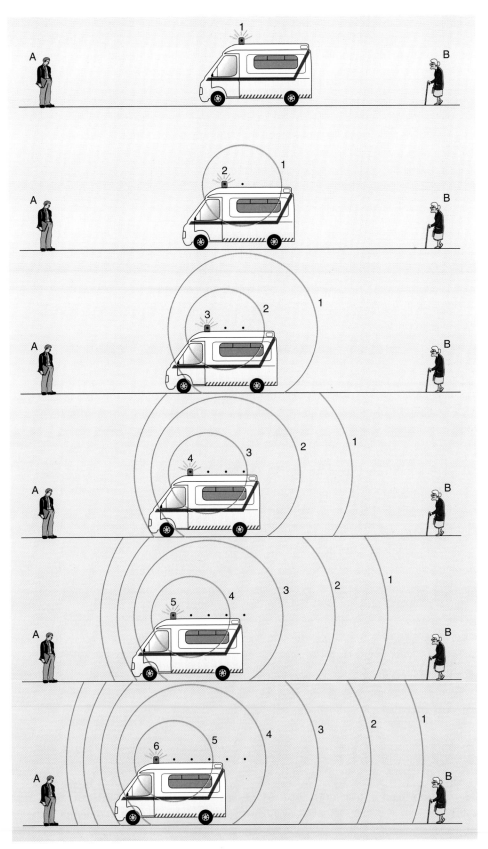

Figure 2.6   A demonstration of the Doppler effect with sound (not to scale). The ambulance sounds its siren as it moves towards observer A. Six successive time intervals are shown in the six sketches, with the curved lines representing successive crests of the sound wave emitted by the siren. By the time the second wave crest is emitted, the ambulance has caught up slightly with the first wave crest. By the time the third wave crest is emitted, the ambulance has caught up with the second wave crest, and so on. The consequence is that a person at A will perceive a sound wave with a shorter wavelength than that emitted by the siren when at rest, whilst a person at B will perceive a longer wavelength.

because the vehicle moves between the time it emits a particular crest of the sound wave and when it emits the next crest. The bunching up in front of the vehicle causes the wavelength of the sound reaching your ears to be shorter than if the vehicle were stationary, and the stretching out behind the vehicle causes the wavelength to be longer.

○ If the wavelength of sound heard from a siren is *shorter* than when the vehicle is stationary, what can be said about the frequency of the sound wave?

○ You know from Block 7 that the wave speed is equal to the wave's frequency multiplied by its wavelength, i.e. $v = f\lambda$. So, as long as the speed of sound remains the same, if its wavelength is smaller (shorter), then its frequency must be larger (higher pitch).

So, as the vehicle approaches, you hear a higher frequency than if the vehicle were stationary. Conversely, as it recedes from you, the frequency will be smaller (a lower pitch) than if the vehicle were stationary. A similar effect is observed with light.

○ The frequency of sound waves may be appreciated by the pitch of the sound perceived by the human ear. How does the frequency of light manifest itself to human senses?

○ The frequency of a light wave is perceived by the human eye as the colour of the light.

A shift in the colour to lower frequencies or longer wavelengths (towards the red end of the spectrum) is an indication of motion away from the observer, a shift in the colour to higher frequencies or shorter wavelengths (towards the blue) is an indication of motion towards the observer.

○ Which way is the spectrum shifted in Figure 2.5c?

○ It is shifted towards longer wavelengths, i.e. towards the red.

Astronomers say that the galaxy spectrum shown in Figure 2.5c displays a **red-shift**, and this is interpreted as an indication that the galaxy is moving away from the Earth. Spectral lines produced in the galaxy by atomic absorption processes have the same frequency and wavelength as lines produced in similar atomic absorption processes in an Earth-based laboratory. But since the galaxy is moving away from the Earth, the wavelengths of its lines observed on Earth are shifted towards the red. By exactly the same reasoning, a spectrum in which features are shifted towards the blue, known not surprisingly as a **blue-shift**, would indicate that the galaxy is moving towards the Earth.

The red-shift, or blue-shift, is specified by a number z which is defined as the *change* in wavelength ($\Delta\lambda$ = observed wavelength minus original wavelength), divided by the original wavelength (λ_0):

$$z = \frac{\Delta\lambda}{\lambda_0} \qquad\qquad (2.5)$$

The original wavelength is assumed to be that which would be produced by the same transitions, in the same elements, in a laboratory on Earth. It is also sometimes known as the *rest wavelength* since it is the wavelength that would be observed from a stationary source. To identify which elements produced the lines in a galaxy spectrum, a certain amount of pattern matching is required to compare whole series of lines rather than just one or two individual lines. The same value of z must apply to *all* lines in a spectrum of a certain galaxy, whatever their individual wavelengths.

For the speeds that we shall be considering here, it can be shown that the red-shift, or blue-shift, is related to the speed of motion of the galaxy v by:

$$z = \frac{v}{c} \tag{2.6}$$

where c is the speed of light, $3.0 \times 10^8 \, \mathrm{m \, s^{-1}}$. So, if the wavelength of a line in the spectrum of a galaxy is measured and compared with the wavelength of the same spectral line, as measured in a laboratory, the red-shift, or blue-shift, of the galaxy can be calculated. This can then be converted into a speed of recession (motion away) or approach (motion towards).

As an illustration of the use of Equations 2.5 and 2.6, look again at Figure 2.5. The spectral lines in the spectrum of the star (Figure 2.5b) occur at the *same* wavelengths as in spectra produced in the laboratory. We can therefore assume that the star is 'at rest' with respect to the Earth. The absorption line labelled C in the spectrum of the star occurs at a wavelength of 431 nm. The corresponding line in the spectrum of the galaxy (Figure 2.5c) occurs at a wavelength of 452 nm. The rest wavelength is therefore 431 nm, and the change in wavelength of this line when observed in the galaxy spectrum is $(452 - 431) \, \mathrm{nm} = 21 \, \mathrm{nm}$. Since the observed wavelength is longer than the rest wavelength, we are dealing with a red-shift here and the galaxy must be receding from us. The red-shift is calculated from Equation 2.5 as $z = \frac{21 \, \mathrm{nm}}{431 \, \mathrm{nm}} = 0.049$. To calculate the speed that this red-shift corresponds to, we rearrange Equation 2.6 to get $v = zc$. (This can be described as the *product* of z and c, since the product of two quantities means one multiplied by the other.) So in this case the recession speed of the galaxy is $v = (0.049 \times 3.0 \times 10^8) \, \mathrm{m \, s^{-1}} = 1.5 \times 10^7 \, \mathrm{m \, s^{-1}}$ or $15\,000 \, \mathrm{km \, s^{-1}}$. (Note that the star which produced the spectrum in Figure 2.5a and b may actually be moving too. However, speeds of up to $70 \, \mathrm{km \, s^{-1}}$ would produce wavelength shifts of less than 0.1 nm, and so would be negligible on the scale of Figure 2.5. So although the star may actually be moving quite fast by everyday standards we can treat it as being at rest in this case.)

Question 2.5   A fast jet aircraft has a red light on its tail that emits light with a wavelength of 656 nm. (a) If the aircraft travels away from you at a speed of $600 \, \mathrm{m \, s^{-1}}$ (about twice the speed of sound), what would be the red-shift of the light reaching you from the tail of the aircraft?

(b) What would be the shift in wavelength of the light that you observe? ($c = 3.0 \times 10^8 \, \mathrm{m \, s^{-1}}$) ◄

Question 2.6   The spectrum of light from a distant galaxy contains absorption lines that are identified as being due to the Balmer series of hydrogen (Block 7, Section 2). A particular line is observed at a wavelength of 500.7 nm, compared with the wavelength of 486.1 nm that would be produced by a source at rest in the laboratory.

(a) Is the galaxy receding from or approaching towards the Earth?

(b) What is the value of z for the galaxy?

(c) What is the speed of the galaxy with respect to the Earth? ($c = 3.0 \times 10^8 \, \mathrm{m \, s^{-1}}$) ◄

Figure 2.7 Edwin Powell Hubble (1889–1953) was an American astronomer who was the first to provide definite proof that the objects we now know as galaxies lie far beyond the Milky Way. He established the speed–distance relationship for distant galaxies, and the constant relating the two is known as the Hubble constant. He also produced a classification scheme for galaxies — dividing them into ellipticals, spirals and barred spirals — based upon their shape. He worked for most of his career at the Mount Wilson Observatory in California. The Hubble Space Telescope, launched by NASA in 1990, is named in his honour.

Our galaxy, the Milky Way, is one member of a small family of nearby galaxies known as the Local Group. Within the Local Group, a variety of red-shifts and blue-shifts are observed. This indicates that, in our local neighbourhood, the galaxies are milling around in a fairly random manner. However, if galaxies and clusters of galaxies that are more distant than the Local Group are observed, a remarkable effect is seen: *all* the galaxies exhibit red-shifts, *none* exhibit blue-shifts.

⬤ Why is this remarkable?

◯ This is remarkable because it shows that *all* clusters of galaxies in the Universe are receding from our own Local Group of galaxies!

2.3 The Hubble relationship

You have seen that the speeds of recession of distant galaxies can be determined by using red-shift measurements, and that their distances may be calculated by comparing the brightnesses of galaxies with their luminosities. When these results are examined for a large number of clusters of galaxies, a quite startling relationship becomes apparent:

The further away a galaxy is, the faster it is moving.

The first person to point this out was the American astronomer Edwin Hubble (Figure 2.7) in 1929. The **Hubble relationship** may be expressed by the simple equation:

$$v = H_0 r \qquad\qquad (2.7)$$

where v is the galaxy's speed, r is its distance from the Local Group, and H_0 is a quantity now known as the **Hubble constant**.

⬤ A rearrangement of Equation 2.7 leads to $H_0 = \dfrac{v}{r}$. Since the units on both sides of an equation must be the same, and given that the speed of recession is typically measured in the unit of km s^{-1}, and the distance to a cluster of galaxies is usually measured in the unit of Mpc, what would be a sensible unit for the Hubble constant?

◯ The unit for speed divided by distance in this case is $\dfrac{\text{km s}^{-1}}{\text{Mpc}}$. So a sensible unit for the Hubble constant is km s^{-1} Mpc^{-1}, and this is in fact what is usually used.

Activity 2.2 The virtual telescope

In order for you to consolidate your understanding of the measurements that lead to the Hubble relationship, you should now work through this CD-ROM activity and derive your own value for the Hubble constant. ◀

Because of the constraints of study time, 'The virtual telescope' only allowed you to make measurements of a maximum of eight clusters of galaxies. Despite this, you should have come up with a value for the Hubble constant which is consistent with the most accurate determinations made today. Figure 2.8 shows a graph of the

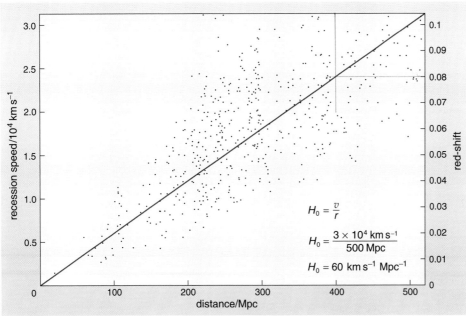

Figure 2.8 The Hubble relationship between the speed of recession of a galaxy and its distance from us, illustrated with a sample of several hundred clusters of galaxies. Note the red-shift scale on the right of the graph; values on this scale are related to the recession speed on the scale on the left by Equation 2.6, $z = v/c$. The large scatter that is apparent in these points reflects the difficulty in accurately determining the recession speed and distance of these clusters. Although error bars are not shown, the red-shifts (and hence speeds) are typically measured to an accuracy of $\pm10\%$, whilst the distances are only accurate to about a factor of two in some cases.

recession speed and distance for several hundred clusters of galaxies. As with your own measurements, a straight line has been drawn through the data points. The gradient of this line gives the value of the Hubble constant as $60\,\mathrm{km\,s^{-1}\,Mpc^{-1}}$.

What does the value for the Hubble constant imply? Well, look at its unit: kilometres per second per megaparsec. This means that for every megaparsec of distance out into the Universe, the galaxies and clusters appear to be moving about $60\,\mathrm{km\,s^{-1}}$ faster.

Question 2.7   Assuming that $H_0 = 60\,\mathrm{km\,s^{-1}\,Mpc^{-1}}$ and $c = 3.0 \times 10^5\,\mathrm{km\,s^{-1}}$, (a) what would be the red-shift of a galaxy at a distance of $400\,\mathrm{Mpc}$ from the Local Group and (b) what would be the distance to a galaxy which has a red-shift of 0.12? ◄

We have only discussed one method for finding the distances to galaxies. In practice other techniques are also used, each appropriate to a range of distances, with one building on the results of another. Because each of these measurements is subject to uncertainty of one sort or another — either in the measurements themselves or the theoretical basis for them — the answers that different people obtain for the Hubble constant do vary significantly. All that can reliably be said is that the Hubble constant probably lies somewhere between 40 and $80\,\mathrm{km\,s^{-1}\,Mpc^{-1}}$. During the lifetime of this course, it is likely that far more precise values for the Hubble constant will be obtained using new generations of powerful telescopes.

2.4 Expanding space

You've seen how cosmologists obtain the observational data on which the Hubble relationship of Equation 2.7 is based. We now turn to a consideration of how it may be interpreted, and then look at the consequences which this interpretation has for the properties of the Universe in the distant past.

Wherever cosmologists look they see galaxies rushing away from the Local Group, and the further away the galaxies are, the faster they appear to move. The interpretation of this is that space *itself* is expanding uniformly, and the same behaviour would be observed *wherever* in the Universe one happened to be. Now, it's quite difficult to appreciate this for our three-dimensional Universe, so, in order to make things simpler, let's consider a one-dimensional case, represented by the strip of elastic shown in Figure 2.9. Showing that uniform expansion of a one-dimensional universe naturally gives rise to the Hubble relationship will hopefully make the idea easier to carry over to the real, three-dimensional case.

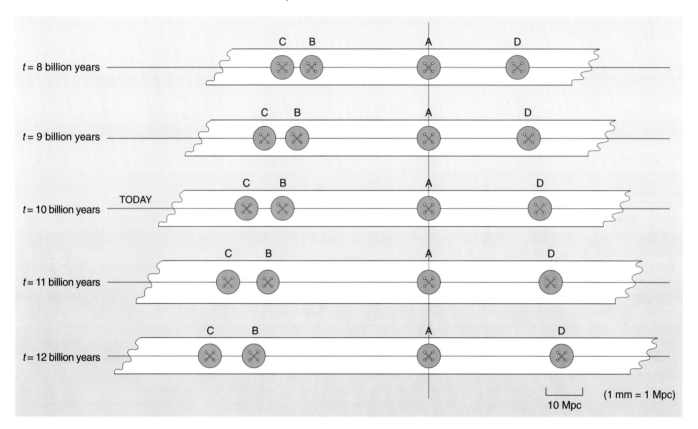

Figure 2.9 A model for the uniform expansion of part of a one-dimensional universe, shown at five time intervals, each one a billion years after the last. The strip of elastic represents space and the buttons sewn onto it, labelled A to D, represent clusters of galaxies. As space expands uniformly so the clusters of galaxies all recede from each other. As explained in the text, the speed at which they recede increases with increasing separation from the point of measurement.

Five time steps are shown in Figure 2.9, each one a billion years after the last, with the third time step identified as 'today'. Moving from one time interval to the next, space (the strip of elastic) expands uniformly, and all the clusters of galaxies (the buttons) get further apart. Imagine that cluster A is the Local Group of galaxies that contains the Milky Way and us. The separation of clusters A and B is 32 Mpc in the first image (represented by 32 mm on Figure 2.9), 36 Mpc in the second image, 40 Mpc in the third image, and so on. (Check these distances by measuring the separations of the 'clusters of galaxies' on Figure 2.9 if you wish.) So clusters A and B are receding from each other at a speed of 4 Mpc every billion years.

Similarly, to an astronomer in cluster A, cluster C appears at distances of 40 Mpc, 45 Mpc, 50 Mpc and so on moving down the sequence. So cluster C is getting further away by 5 Mpc every billion years. This is a faster speed of recession than that for cluster B, and is merely a consequence of it being further away. To an astronomer in cluster A, cluster D appears at distances of 24 Mpc, 27 Mpc, 30 Mpc and so on moving down the sequence. So cluster D is getting further away by 3 Mpc every billion years — slower than both clusters B and C since it's nearer.

The model works well for measurements from cluster A, which we can imagine to be the Local Group of galaxies, but how do things look to an Amoeboid Zingatularian astronomer in cluster B? Well, to it cluster A is clearly receding at 4 Mpc every billion years, but cluster C is receding at only 1 Mpc every billion years. Well, that's fine because cluster C is much closer than cluster A and so has a smaller recession speed. Similarly, cluster D is receding from cluster B at a speed of 7 Mpc every billion years. And that too is just what would be expected, since cluster D is further from cluster B than either A or C.

Wherever you happen to be in this one-dimensional universe, clusters that are further away from you recede at larger and larger speeds, and the recession speed is proportional to the distance, just as described by the Hubble relationship.

Activity 2.3   Understanding the Hubble relationship

This activity will help you to appreciate the relationships between recession speed, red-shift, and the Hubble constant for the one-dimensional universe in Figure 2.9. ◄

What was demonstrated in one-dimension with Figure 2.9 is also true in the real three-dimensional Universe in which we live, it's just a little harder to visualize, and we won't attempt to do so here.

Having interpreted the Hubble relationship to mean that space is expanding, we can now look at the consequences of this phenomenon. It is believed that the amount of matter in the Universe is constant. So, since the separation between distant galaxies is continually increasing, this implies that the mean density of the Universe — the mass per unit volume — is continually falling.

> In other words, in the distant past the Universe was very dense, whereas now, the mean density is rather low. This is the first important piece of evidence as to the conditions that prevailed in the early Universe.

2.5   A few strange ideas

When discussing the overall structure of the Universe, some rather awkward questions often arise. In the discussion below these will be addressed in the hope that it will answer any questions you have about the behaviour of our expanding Universe. Before starting though, you should be warned that you will be required to put aside some 'common sense' notions of reality and accept a few ideas that may at first seem rather strange. As you will see, it is not only artists and poets that need fertile and wide-ranging imaginations — such characteristics are equally useful for cosmologists!

2.5.1   Limitations

The first complication is that the Hubble constant was larger in the distant past than it is today. (The subscript '0' in H_0 tells us that we are dealing with the value 'now'.) There are two reasons for this. First, as you saw in the one-dimensional universe analogy (Activity 2.3), even if galaxies keep moving apart with a constant speed, the Hubble constant decreases as time progresses because it is inversely proportional to the separation between distant objects. Second, the expansion rate of the Universe is continually slowing down, due to the gravitational attraction between all the matter in the Universe. This phenomenon is referred to as **deceleration**, and further reduces the value of the Hubble constant as time progresses. The precise value of the deceleration is not known, so consequently the distance scale of the Universe in the past is also uncertain.

Also, a word of caution is called for concerning the limitations of Equations 2.6 and 2.7. Although the formulae developed in Sections 2.1–2.4 are adequate for the discussion in the rest of the block, it would be wrong to assume that they apply in every situation. In fact, Equations 2.6 and 2.7 are only true when the recession speeds and distances involved are less than about 20% of the speed of light and 1 Gpc, respectively. For galaxies receding faster than this, the simple formulation of Equation 2.6 breaks down (i.e. it gives the wrong answer) and the theory proposed by Einstein (known as special relativity) must be used to derive an accurate relationship between red-shift and speed. Furthermore, at high recession speeds, the physical meaning of 'distance' in the Universe needs to be considered carefully. The light that we now see from rapidly receding galaxies was emitted by them when the Universe was much younger than it is now. In the time it has taken that light to reach us, the Universe has expanded and so distances between galaxies have changed. Therefore, care has to be taken in interpreting the distances that are measured in an expanding universe when recession speeds are a significant fraction of the speed of light. However, at low recession speeds, the quantity r in Equation 2.7 does correspond to our everyday idea of distance.

For these reasons, cosmologists don't usually refer to the speed and distance of rapidly receding, very distant galaxies, but to their red-shift and *look-back time*. This latter quantity is the time taken for the light emitted by a galaxy to reach us, and indicates how far back in time we are seeing. Looking at objects far away means that we are actually looking back in time, because the light that we see was emitted by the object in the distant past, and has taken a substantial amount of time to reach us. For instance, assuming a Hubble constant of $60 \, \text{km s}^{-1} \, \text{Mpc}^{-1}$ and the most likely value for the deceleration, a galaxy with a red-shift of $z = 3$, has a recession speed of 88% of the speed of light (not three times the speed of light as predicted by Equation 2.6), and is situated at a look-back time of 9.5 billion years. We are seeing the galaxy as it was 9.5 billion years ago, since it has taken that long for the light emitted by the galaxy to reach us. Neither Equation 2.6 nor Equation 2.7 applies in this regime.

2.5.2 Concepts

In response to the claim that space is expanding uniformly, many people ask (not unreasonably) 'What is the Universe expanding into?' In fact, the expansion of the Universe is interpreted very differently from an expansion of matter *into* space; rather it is interpreted as an expansion *of space itself*. Space is a property of the Universe, and matter is (more or less) fixed in a space that expands. This was illustrated by the one-dimensional universe analogy of Figure 2.9: the elastic (space) expands uniformly, but the buttons (clusters of galaxies) remain the same size and shape, they are merely carried along by the universal expansion. Similarly, we are not expanding, nor is the Earth, the Solar System, the Milky Way, or even our Local Group of galaxies. These objects are all bound together by electric and gravitational forces of attraction between the atoms and molecules of which they are composed. Only beyond the scale of clusters of galaxies does the expansion win.

Now, although the red-shift of distant galaxies has been described as being comparable to a Doppler shift, it is important to realize that there is one vital difference between a 'standard' Doppler red-shift (such as that caused by the random motion of galaxies in the Local Group) and what may be called a 'cosmological' red-shift. The Doppler effect is the result of the motion of an object *through* space at a certain speed; whereas cosmological red-shifts are caused by the expansion *of* space itself. So, even though a distant cluster of galaxies may have a recession speed that is 88% of the speed of light, that cluster is not moving rapidly with respect to its local surroundings. In terms of the analogy in Figure 2.9, the buttons on the strip of elastic are not moving with respect to the local patch of elastic. It is the expansion of space itself that 'stretches out' the wavelength of the emitted light as it travels through space. The more space there is between the object emitting the light and the point of observation, the bigger the 'stretch', and so the larger the red-shift.

Another question that many people ask is: 'Where in the Universe is the centre of this expansion?' Well, there is no centre of expansion — all space is expanding at the same rate in all directions, and the same expansion would be measured wherever you happened to be. Perhaps another analogy will help here. Figure 2.10 shows a two-dimensional universe — one step up in complexity from that shown in Figure 2.9, but still one-dimension short of the real thing. Here the Universe is represented as the two-dimensional surface of a balloon, with the buttons stuck on the surface representing the clusters of galaxies as before. It is only the *surface* of this balloon that represents space — everything inside or outside of the balloon is not part of this universe. As space expands (i.e. as the balloon is inflated), the clusters of galaxies move further apart with their recession speeds increasing with distance just as in Figure 2.9. But the centre of expansion (the centre of the balloon) does not lie anywhere within the universe. Our own three-dimensional Universe also has no centre of expansion. The problem is that none of us can think in enough dimensions to visualize it properly. *This is an important point: do not even attempt to visualize the corresponding situation for our own three-dimensional Universe. It is simply not possible to do so!*

Perhaps there is a simple answer to the question 'How big is the Universe?' Well, there is a simple answer, but it's not easy to comprehend. The Universe is probably infinite in extent — and always has been. (The balloon analogy is therefore misleading in this respect, since that describes a Universe with finite size.) The Universe was infinite at the instant of its creation, and has remained infinite ever since. When it is said that space is expanding, you should *not* interpret this to mean that the overall *size* of the Universe is increasing (if it's infinite it can't get any bigger since infinity is the biggest possible). Rather, you should interpret it to mean that the *separation* of large structures within the Universe is increasing — in other words galaxies are getting further apart. The size of the Universe probably is, was and ever will be, infinite.

A popular misconception is to think of the Universe as originating at a 'point in space' and expanding from there. This is quite the wrong visual image, and you should try not to think in these terms. Remember, space is a property of the Universe, not something within which the Universe sits. Furthermore, the entire infinite space of the Universe, and the raw materials from which the galaxies were built, were all created at the same instant. The separations between objects increase with time, as they are carried along by the expansion of the space that was created at the instant the Universe began. Again, don't even attempt to visualize an infinite, expanding three-dimensional Universe — it's simply impossible for anyone to do!

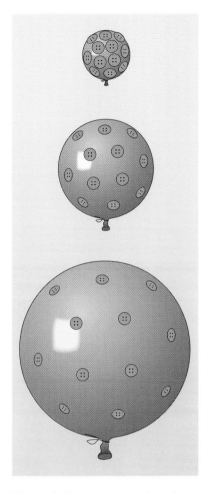

Figure 2.10 The expansion of a (finite) two-dimensional universe visualized as the surface of an inflating balloon. Notice that the centre of expansion does not lie anywhere in the two-dimensional space of this universe (the surface of the balloon).

A final point is that there is no edge to the Universe either. Since the Universe is (probably) infinite then, by definition, it goes on forever and travelling in a straight line you would never reach an edge. Even if the Universe were finite in size though, you would never reach an edge either. Travelling in a straight line in a finite Universe, you would eventually end up back where you started, just as an ant would crawling over the surface of the two-dimensional universe model in Figure 2.10.

The preceding few paragraphs provide a rather mind-bending excursion for most people! The problem is that we are only used to comprehending things on a much smaller scale of time and space than is necessary to properly grasp the immensity of the Universe. The ideas can be expressed mathematically, but would be an unnecessary and lengthy detour from the main story. Nevertheless, the basic ideas are not so difficult if you are prepared to discard some ideas that are 'common sense' in our everyday experience. To summarize, the Universe is probably infinite, with no centre and no edge. It makes no sense to ask what is 'outside' the Universe, because space is a property of the Universe itself, and doesn't exist elsewhere. Space itself is expanding uniformly such that the separation between distant galaxies increases with time, and the overall density of the Universe decreases. A consequence of this uniform expansion is that the speed of recession increases with increasing distance from the place of measurement.

2.6   The age of the Universe

For the time being let's follow this first big clue of cosmology: space is expanding and therefore in the past all the galaxies were closer together than they are now. If we make the assumption that all the galaxies we can see have been moving at their present speeds since the Universe began, then we can use the Hubble constant to calculate a rough age for the Universe. Galaxies that are currently a distance r apart, and moving away from each other with a speed v, would have been 'zero distance apart' at a time $\dfrac{r}{v}$ in the past (remember time = $\dfrac{\text{distance}}{\text{speed}}$). But from Equation 2.7, $\dfrac{r}{v}$ is simply $\dfrac{1}{H_0}$. So the quantity $t_0 = \dfrac{1}{H_0}$ provides a rough value for the age of the Universe, assuming that the expansion rate has been constant since time began.

The value of the Hubble constant currently accepted by most cosmologists is about $60\,\text{km}\,\text{s}^{-1}\,\text{Mpc}^{-1}$. So

$$t_0 = \frac{1}{60\,\text{km}\,\text{s}^{-1}\,\text{Mpc}^{-1}} = 0.017\,\text{Mpc}\,\text{s}\,\text{km}^{-1}$$

To convert this rather odd unit into something useful, we note that $1.0\,\text{Mpc} = 3.1 \times 10^{19}\,\text{km}$, so

$$t_0 = (0.017\,\text{Mpc}\,\text{s}\,\text{km}^{-1}) \times (3.1 \times 10^{19}\,\text{km}\,\text{Mpc}^{-1}) = 5.3 \times 10^{17}\,\text{s}$$

Since one year is equivalent to about $3.2 \times 10^7\,\text{s}$, expressing this time as an equivalent number of years results in a value of:

$$t_0 = \frac{5.3 \times 10^{17}\,\text{s}}{3.2 \times 10^7\,\text{s}\,\text{y}^{-1}} = 1.7 \times 10^{10}\,\text{y or 17 billion years (to two sig figs)}$$

In practice, the true age of the Universe must be somewhat less than the value given by $\dfrac{1}{H_0}$ because the gravitational attraction between all the matter in the Universe has slowed down the expansion as time has progressed. (In other words the value of the Hubble constant was larger in the past than it is today.) The most likely value for this deceleration leads to a value for the age of the Universe that is two-thirds of the value calculated above — or about 11 billion years. And that is not so long ago — it's only about twice the age of the Sun and the Earth.

Question 2.8 Use the value for the Hubble constant that you determined in Activity 2.2 to calculate your own value for the age of the Universe, following the procedure above. ◀

2.7 Summary of Section 2

The distance r from the Local Group to a cluster of galaxies may be determined using the relationship between the brightness of its tenth brightest member F_{10} and the standard luminosity of that galaxy L_{10}:

$$r = \sqrt{\frac{L_{10}}{4\pi F_{10}}} \tag{2.3}$$

The procedure is based on the assumption that the tenth brightest galaxies in all clusters have the *same* luminosity. Distances to galaxies and clusters of galaxies are measured in units of kpc, Mpc or Gpc.

The red-shift z of a galaxy is defined as the shift in the wavelength $\Delta\lambda$ of a spectral line seen in its spectrum, divided by the rest wavelength λ_0 of that line:

$$z = \frac{\Delta\lambda}{\lambda_0} \tag{2.5}$$

The speed of recession v of a distant galaxy is related to its red-shift by:

$$z = \frac{v}{c} \tag{2.6}$$

where c is the speed of light.

All galaxies beyond the Local Group exhibit red-shifts, so all distant galaxies are receding from us. Moreover, the speed of recession is greater for galaxies that are further away. The Hubble relationship expresses this dependence:

$$v = H_0 r \tag{2.7}$$

The Hubble constant, H_0, is measured to be around $60\,\text{km}\,\text{s}^{-1}\,\text{Mpc}^{-1}$.

The Hubble relationship is a consequence of the fact that space itself is expanding uniformly. Since the separation of distant objects is increasing with time, the mean density of the Universe is continually falling. Extrapolating the observed expansion back in time leads us to believe that the Universe originated about 11 billion years ago.

The Universe is probably infinite in size, and always has been; it has no centre, since the same expansion would be measured from any location within it; it has no edge because space is a property of the Universe itself and does not exist elsewhere.

3 The cooling Universe

Having looked closely at the expansion of the Universe, we will now examine the other major piece of evidence for an evolving Universe, namely the observation that the Universe is gradually cooling.

A discussion of the fact that the Universe is cooling implies that the Universe must have a temperature, and that may seem a rather strange concept. It makes sense to talk about the temperature at the centre or surface of the Sun or the Earth, but what is the temperature of the Universe as a whole? After all, nowadays the Universe largely consists of almost empty space between the galaxies. However, space is not as empty as you might suppose: on average it contains about 400 million photons per cubic metre. This is the 'heat radiation' of the Universe and its spectrum corresponds to a particular temperature.

○ What is a photon?

○ A photon is a 'particle' of electromagnetic radiation (Block 7). It carries a certain amount of energy referred to as a quantum.

3.1 Black-body radiation

When an oven is heated up, it radiates energy in the form of photons. These photons have a range of energies but the precise distribution of photons — the relative number that are emitted with any particular energy — depends on the temperature of the oven. As you know, the distribution of photons plotted against photon energy is simply the spectrum of the radiation. In Block 7 you saw that as the temperature of an object increases, so it emits photons of higher and higher energies. There will still be a distribution of photons with different energies, but the *mean* photon energy will shift to higher values. An object whose emission has a mean photon energy in the blue part of the spectrum will be hotter than one whose emission has a mean photon energy in the red part of the spectrum, for instance. But there is no need to restrict this relationship between photon energy and temperature to merely the visible part of the electromagnetic spectrum. At higher energies (shorter wavelengths) than blue light there are the ultraviolet and X-ray regions. Objects whose emission has a mean photon energy in these parts of the spectrum must be extremely hot. Conversely, at lower energies (longer wavelengths) than red light are the infrared and microwave regions. Emission which has a mean photon energy in these ranges would indicate much cooler temperatures.

The continuous spectral distributions of many objects have precisely the same shape, they are merely shifted to different energies or wavelengths. You have, in fact, already met examples of such spectra both in Block 2, where the emission spectra of the Sun and Earth were discussed, and in Block 7, where continuous spectra were first described. Some more examples are shown in Figure 3.1 and each of these is what is known as a **black-body spectrum** or thermal spectrum.

As you saw in the experiment described in Block 2 Activity 5.1, a black surface absorbs more radiation than a silver surface. In fact, a perfectly black surface will absorb all the radiation that falls upon it and, in a steady-state (or equilibrium) situation, where it maintains a constant temperature, it will also emit all this radiation back again. (We are assuming that the surface is in a vacuum and cannot exchange

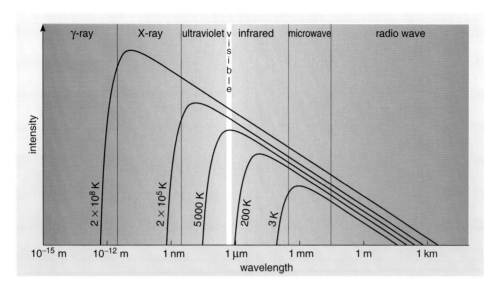

Figure 3.1 The black-body spectra emitted by objects at temperatures of 2×10^8 K, 2×10^5 K, 5 000 K, 200 K and 3 K. (Refer to Block 5 if you need reminding about the absolute (Kelvin) temperature scale.) The scale along the bottom shows the wavelength of the radiation, and you can see that hotter objects emit more of their radiation at shorter wavelengths. Note that the wavelengths and intensities are plotted on 'powers-of-ten' scales to allow a vast range to be included in one diagram.

energy with its surroundings in any other way.) The phrase 'black body' is therefore used as a shorthand to describe any object that behaves as a perfect absorber and emitter of radiation. The crucial features of black-body spectra are that they all have the same continuous shape, they contain no emission or absorption lines, and the mean photon energy (or corresponding wavelength and frequency) depends *only* on the temperature of the object.

Question 3.1 Use Figure 3.1 to answer the following questions.

(a) An object at a temperature of 300 K (equivalent to that of a warm day) radiates a black-body spectrum. In which region of the electromagnetic spectrum would the peak intensity of this spectrum occur?

(b) The black-body spectrum emitted by an object has a peak intensity in the X-ray part of the electromagnetic spectrum. Roughly what is the temperature of the object? ◄

The key to understanding how black-body spectra are produced is that the object and the radiation are in *thermal equilibrium*. As much radiation is being absorbed as is being emitted at every instant, and the object therefore remains at a constant temperature. We can therefore say that the radiation also possesses this same temperature. The conditions necessary to create such a situation are generally those of high temperatures and large amounts of energy. Under such conditions, photons are rapidly absorbed and re-emitted by matter.

⬤ In order for a photon to be absorbed by an atom, what condition must be met with regard to the energy levels of the atom?

◯ There must be a pair of energy levels whose separation is equal to the energy of the photon concerned (Block 7 Section 2).

⬤ How could you guarantee that a photon of virtually *any* energy could be absorbed?

◯ There must be a great many energy levels, very close together, and extending over a large range of energy.

Recall from Block 7 Section 2 that this situation will exist when atoms are ionized, so that a continuum of energy levels exists, and also when atoms are arranged in a metal

Figure 3.2 Ludwig Boltzmann (1844–1906) was an Austrian theoretical physicist who derived several key equations relating the microscopic properties of atoms to their temperature. The Boltzmann constant k appears in most of these equations. Hostile reviews of his work by influential colleagues caused him to suffer from depression in his later life. He killed himself in 1906, only a few years before most of the scientific community accepted his theories, which are now cornerstones of physics.

which has a continuous energy band. So, in either of these cases, photons of *all* energies may be absorbed and emitted, and a continuous spectrum is produced. The continuous spectrum of the Sun and other stars (ignoring the absorption lines superimposed on top) may be approximated by black-body spectra.

If an astronomer observes a black-body spectrum of radiation, and then measures its mean photon energy, the temperature of the source of the radiation can be unambiguously determined. This is because there is a precise relationship between mean photon energy and temperature, namely:

$$E_{\text{ph,mean}} = 2.7kT \tag{3.1}$$

The constant of proportionality that links energy and temperature is known as the Boltzmann constant, represented by the symbol k (see Figure 3.2). This constant has a value of about $1.4 \times 10^{-23}\,\text{J K}^{-1}$, or $8.6 \times 10^{-5}\,\text{eV K}^{-1}$ in alternative units. Note that the mean photon energy for any temperature is similar to the energy at which the peak intensity of a spectrum occurs, but not quite the same, since black-body spectra are not symmetrical either side of the peak (see Figure 3.1). The reason why the factor of 2.7 appears in Equation 3.1 is related to this complication and to the fact that the Boltzmann constant itself is actually defined in a different context which is not relevant to the present discussion.

Question 3.2 A black-body spectrum is observed with a mean photon energy of 1.4 eV. What is the temperature of the object that is responsible for producing this spectrum? ◀

Question 3.3 An object at a temperature of $10^5\,\text{K}$ emits a black-body spectrum. What is the wavelength corresponding to the photons that have the mean energy of the radiation of this spectrum? In which part of the electromagnetic spectrum does this lie? (*Hint*: Use the Boltzmann constant $k = 8.6 \times 10^{-5}\,\text{eV K}^{-1}$ to convert from temperature into energy; use the Planck constant $h = 4.1 \times 10^{-15}\,\text{eV Hz}^{-1}$ to convert from energy into frequency; and finally use the speed of light $c = 3.0 \times 10^8\,\text{m s}^{-1}$ to convert from frequency into wavelength.) ◀

3.2 The cosmic microwave background

Objects in the Universe emit electromagnetic radiation across the whole spectrum from radio waves through infrared, visible radiation, ultraviolet, and X-rays to γ-rays. The spectra from individual objects are, in some cases, characteristic of thermal processes, and so have the continuous black-body shape. If astronomers observe the Universe in the microwave part of the spectrum — that is at wavelengths of a few millimetres — a remarkable phenomenon is observed. What they detect is a background microwave 'glow' coming from the whole Universe, and wherever they look (away from individual stars or galaxies) it has virtually the same spectral distribution and intensity. Moreover, the shape of the spectrum is that of a thermal or black-body source. This **cosmic microwave background**, or CMB, was discovered in 1964 by Arno Penzias and Robert Wilson (Figure 3.3).

Over the years since Penzias and Wilson first discovered the CMB, its spectrum and variation across the sky have been investigated and mapped with increasing accuracy. Some of the most recent measurements, and the most accurate, are those made using

Figure 3.3 Wilson and Penzias standing by the antenna with which they discovered the cosmic microwave background at Bell Telephone Laboratories in New Jersey, USA. They were tracking a satellite and found that their antenna picked up not only the signal from the satellite, but also some background 'noise'. What they discovered was that this noise came from all over the sky. After consultations with physicists from Princeton University, they realized that they had inadvertently discovered the 'heat radiation' of the Universe. Their work played a major part in establishing the standard model of the origin and early evolution of the Universe.

the Cosmic Background Explorer (COBE) satellite, which was launched in 1989. The average spectrum of the radiation, over the whole sky, measured by COBE is shown in Figure 3.4. The observations are an excellent fit with the theoretical curve that would be expected from a black-body source at a temperature of 2.73 K.

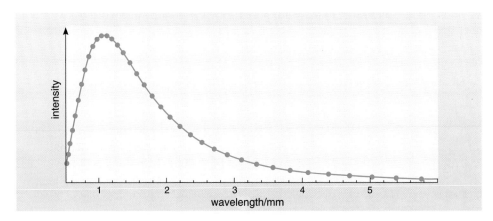

Figure 3.4 The spectrum of the cosmic microwave background radiation as measured by COBE. The points are the measured data, and the line drawn through them is a black-body spectrum corresponding to a temperature of 2.73 K. Error bars on each point are too small to be displayed. The wavelength corresponding to the mean photon energy of the spectrum is about 2 mm. (Notice that whereas Figure 3.1 was drawn on a powers-of-ten scale in order to display the vast range of wavelengths across the electromagnetic spectrum, this graph is plotted on a simple linear scale. For this reason the shape of the spectrum here appears different to that of the black-body spectra in Figure 3.1.)

In precise physical terms, the temperature of the CMB radiation is now (coincidentally) one hundred times colder than the normal melting temperature of ice (273 K). Yet, the spectrum has exactly the same shape as is observed in, say, a furnace whose walls are at a temperature of 3 000 K, where interactions between radiation and matter rapidly create the stable distribution of photon energies necessary to produce a black-body spectrum.

⬤   What is the mean photon energy of the CMB radiation?

◯   This radiation corresponds to a temperature of 2.73 K. So, using Equation 3.1, the mean photon energy is

$$E_{ph,mean} = 2.7 \times (8.6 \times 10^{-5}\,eV\,K^{-1}) \times (2.73\,K) = 6.3 \times 10^{-4}\,eV$$

At a temperature of only 2.73 K, a steady state, or thermal equilibrium between matter and radiation in the Universe is virtually impossible to establish since the energy of most of the photons is so very small when compared with the separation of energy levels in hydrogen atoms. So how can radiation that is now far too cold to interact with matter, to any significant extent, have acquired a thermal spectrum, when thermal spectra are generally characteristic of processes at least a thousand times hotter? Were it not for the previous observation of an expanding Universe, there would be a real puzzle here.

If you take any sample of gas, and allow it to expand without putting any energy in or extracting any energy, the temperature of the gas will fall. Now, the Universe may be thought of as just such a sample of gas. As the Universe grows older, so space expands. No energy is put into or removed from the Universe, so the overall temperature of the Universe naturally falls with time. Bearing this in mind, the solution to the problem above is rather simple: when the CMB radiation was last in equilibrium with matter in the Universe, it was a thousand times hotter. The thousandfold cooling since then was produced by the expansion of the Universe (or, more properly, of space itself). In other words, the CMB radiation we now see was emitted by matter at a time in the distant past when the Universe was much hotter than it is today.

Another (entirely equivalent) way to look at this is in terms of red-shift. As the CMB radiation travels towards us from distant parts of the Universe, so the wavelength of the radiation is red-shifted by the expansion of the intervening space. Looking back to the time when the CMB radiation and matter were last in equilibrium with each other entails a red-shift of about one thousand. In other words, the wavelength corresponding to the mean photon energy of the CMB radiation that we see today (about 2 mm) was a thousand times shorter (i.e. it was about 2 μm) when the radiation was emitted. The wavelength of the radiation has been 'stretched out' by the expansion of the Universe.

Since wavelength is inversely proportional to photon energy (Block 7 Section 9), a lengthening of the wavelength corresponds to a reduction in photon energy. So the expansion of the Universe has shifted the mean photon energy of the radiation, from the infrared part of the spectrum, down into the microwave region where it is observed today.

The CMB radiation is therefore a relic of the time when radiation and matter in the Universe existed in equilibrium, at a temperature of around 3 000 K. The CMB photons pervade the entire Universe, wherever astronomers look. This indicates that the entire Universe was once at a much higher temperature.

3.3 The hot big bang model for the origin of the Universe

The expansion of the Universe (as expressed by the Hubble relationship) tells us that objects in the Universe were closer together in the past than they are today. In other words, the Universe was denser in the past than it is now. The cosmic microwave background radiation tells us that the Universe was hotter in the past than it is now. These are the two main pieces of evidence pointing to the fact that our Universe originated in, what has become known as, a **Big Bang**. The standard model for the origin and early evolution of the Universe is sometimes known as the *hot big bang model*. Space and time were created in this event, and space has expanded as time has progressed ever since. The story of the evolution of the Universe from the time of the Big Bang to the present day and beyond will be presented in Sections 11 and 12. However, in order to discuss such an immense topic, it is necessary to appreciate the role that four fundamental interactions each play in the evolution of the Universe. In the next few sections you will learn about these four interactions in turn, and in Section 10 you will discover how attempts are being made to unify these into a single, coherent, theory of everything.

3.4 Summary of Section 3

The radiation emitted by an object in thermal equilibrium has a black-body spectrum, and this continuous spectrum has a characteristic shape. The mean photon energy of a black-body spectrum is determined solely by the temperature of the body — higher temperature objects have spectra with a higher mean photon energy. The relationship between mean photon energy and temperature is given by

$$E_{\text{ph,mean}} = 2.7kT \tag{3.1}$$

where k is the Boltzmann constant, $8.6 \times 10^{-5}\,\text{eV K}^{-1}$.

Wherever astronomers look in the Universe they see a 'glow' of radiation known as the cosmic microwave background (CMB). The black-body spectrum of this radiation corresponds to a temperature of only 2.73 K. This radiation has been red-shifted to longer wavelengths (cooler temperatures) by the expansion of the Universe and indicates that the Universe was much hotter in the past than it is now.

The expansion and cooling of the Universe point to the fact that the Universe was both denser and hotter in the past. It is believed that time and space were created in an event referred to as the Big Bang.

4 Four fundamental interactions

In Section 11 you will get a fuller picture of what the Universe was (most probably) like when the cosmic background radiation interacted readily with matter (long before the formation of the first galaxies and stars). It is even possible to give a reasonable account of much earlier epochs. But first, we need to summarize what is known about the interactions of matter and radiation, from experiments performed at energies achievable on Earth. These in turn suggest some things that might occur at kinetic energies higher than we can achieve on Earth, but which were probably very common in the early Universe.

Thus we need to turn, for a while, from the very large — the Universe itself — to the very small — the structure of the atom. This reflects the dramatic interplay between cosmology and high-energy particle physics in recent decades: each informs the other. Cosmologists have learned things from the cosmic microwave background radiation which challenge particle physicists to conjecture about interactions of particles at energies higher than those achievable in the laboratory. Particle physicists extrapolate their understanding of theories developed to explain laboratory results and then turn back to the Universe for evidence against which to test these theories.

⬤ Which two observed features of the Universe, described in Sections 2 and 3, suggest that in its past it would have been a good laboratory for particle physics?

◯ The Universe is expanding (Section 2) and cooling (Section 3), so in the past it was denser and hotter, and particle interactions would have been more frequent and more violent.

In Section 11 you will find that all of the particle physics which you learned in Block 7, and the extensions of it in this block, is needed to tell the best current version of the history of our Universe. It turns out that what is needed is a quantum theory of the interactions — or forces — between particles, and an understanding of how they change their character when the participating particles interact at high kinetic energies. In outlining this, we shall refer to **four fundamental interactions**, each of which you have already met earlier in the course.

1   **Electromagnetic interactions**: as you saw in Block 7, these are responsible for the forces between electrons and protons in atoms, and for the emission and absorption of electromagnetic radiation, such as light. A small leftover electromagnetic interaction of the electrons and protons in atoms allows atoms to bind together to make molecules (Block 8).

2   **Strong interactions**: as you saw in Block 7, these provide the (very) strong force between quarks in hadrons, such as between the up (u) and down (d) quarks in the proton (uud) and neutron (udd). A small residual strong interaction between quarks binds nucleons in the nuclei of atoms.

3   **Weak interactions**: again as you saw in Block 7, these are responsible for processes, such as β-decay, which involve both quarks and leptons. For example, in the process of nuclear β^--decay, a down quark (d) in a neutron (udd) turns into an up quark (u) to make a proton (uud). A pair of leptons is emitted, in this case an electron, e^-, and its associated antineutrino, $\overline{\nu}_e$.

4   **Gravitational interactions**: these make apples fall, maintain planets in their orbits around stars (Block 3), and slow down the expansion of the Universe. However, they are negligible within the atom. But when matter aggregates into huge (and electrically neutral) lumps, such as planets and stars, gravity holds sway. You will see that it also holds some surprises, undreamt of by Newton.

These four interactions are the subjects of Sections 5–8. We will look at the way in which these interactions operate, and also at how their strengths may be characterized in terms of so-called dimensionless numbers. In Section 9 you will study the four interactions at work in our local power station, the Sun. In Section 10, you will learn that these interactions are not as distinct as had been previously supposed: some (perhaps all) of them may be different aspects of a more unified description of nature, appearing to us as different as ice, water, and steam, yet deriving from the same basic principles. In Section 11, the ideas of Sections 2–10 will be woven into a tapestry history of the Universe.

We will begin this journey from large to small, and back to large, by relating familiar phenomena to the four interactions.

Question 4.1   For each of the following processes, identify a principal role played by one of the four fundamental interactions. If possible, give examples of roles played by one or more of the other three interactions in each case. (a) A child bouncing on a trampoline; (b) turning on an electric light in a darkened room; (c) sunbathing; (d) cancer therapies, such as chemotherapy and radiotherapy. ◀

Activity 4.1   *Revision: fundamental particles*

This activity allows you to revise more of the material from Block 7 in order to prepare yourself for the remainder of Block 11. ◀

Activity 4.2   *Planning your study time*

This activity allows you to think about planning your study time for the rest of Block 11, now that you are approaching the end of the course. ◀

5 Electromagnetic interactions

Atomic (Block 7) and molecular (Block 8) processes involve the interaction between charged particles, such as that which occurs between electrons and protons in an atom. These electromagnetic interactions, which are at the origin of all atomic and molecular activity, have two aspects: electric forces between charged objects, and magnetic forces between moving charges (i.e. electric currents). Electromagnetic radiation (such as light) is emitted or absorbed (as photons) in processes involving these forces. This radiation propagates as a wave with a speed $c = 2.998 \times 10^8 \, \text{m s}^{-1}$ (to four significant figures), which is a universal constant of nature, i.e. it has the same value throughout the Universe.

These three features of electromagnetic interactions — electric forces, magnetic forces, and electromagnetic radiation — will now feature in turn, in Sections 5.1–5.3. Our aim is to develop a thumbnail sketch of their unification, in the modern theory of quantum electrodynamics (QED), which is the subject of Section 5.4.

5.1 Electric forces

5.1.1 Coulomb's law

The law which describes the force of electrical attraction and repulsion was discovered by Charles Augustin de Coulomb in 1785 (Figure 5.1), and can be expressed as follows:

> **Coulomb's law**: Two particles of unlike (or like) charge, at rest, separated by a distance r, attract (or repel) each other with an electric force that is inversely proportional to the square of their separation and is proportional to the product of the charges.

Coulomb's law can be put in the form of an equation by inserting a constant into the proportionality described above:

$$F_e = -k_e \frac{Q_1 Q_2}{r^2} \tag{5.1}$$

where F_e is the attractive force between the two charges Q_1 and Q_2, and k_e is a constant that we'll call the Coulomb constant. Notice the minus sign on the right-hand side of the equation. When F_e is negative, the force between the charges is repulsive, and when it is positive, the force is attractive. Let's explore what Coulomb's law implies about the forces between charged particles.

- If the charge Q_1 of one particle doubles, what happens to the force between the two charged particles?

- The force also doubles, since it is proportional to the charge Q_1.

- If two charged particles are moved twice as far apart, what happens to the force between them?

- The force is reduced by a factor of four, since it is inversely proportional to the square of the separation.

Figure 5.1 Charles Augustin de Coulomb (1736–1806) was a French physicist who worked on many areas of science, although it is for his work on electric forces that he is best remembered. He developed the 'inverse square law' for describing electrical attraction and repulsion, which led to the definition of electric charge. The SI unit of electric charge is named the coulomb in his honour.

○ What does the minus sign in Equation 5.1 tell us about the forces between charges with opposite signs and between charges with the same sign?

○ If one particle has a positive charge and the other has a negative charge (i.e. unlike charges) there is a positive force of attraction, since the product Q_1Q_2 is negative. If the particles have charges with the same sign (both positive or both negative), an overall minus sign remains, and the force between them is repulsive.

In other words, unlike charges attract, and like charges repel each other.

As you saw in Block 5, the SI unit of electric charge is the coulomb, which has the symbol C. The value of the Coulomb constant, when the charges are separated by empty space (a vacuum), is $k_e = 8.988 \times 10^9\,\mathrm{N\,m^2\,C^{-2}}$, to four significant figures.

○ Verify that the appropriate SI unit for the Coulomb constant is $\mathrm{N\,m^2\,C^{-2}}$.

○ Equation 5.1 may be rearranged to make k_e the subject,

$$k_e = -\frac{F_e r^2}{Q_1 Q_2}$$

The units on the right-hand side of this equation are

$$\frac{\mathrm{N} \times \mathrm{m}^2}{\mathrm{C} \times \mathrm{C}} \text{ or } \mathrm{N\,m^2\,C^{-2}}$$

Since the units on both sides of an equation must be the same, this must also be the unit for k_e.

Before trying Question 5.1, read Box 5.1, *Orders of magnitude*.

Box 5.1 *Orders of magnitude*

When doing calculations in science, it is sometimes not necessary or appropriate to deal with numbers to an accuracy of even one significant figure. Often, when we need an approximate answer, all we need to consider is the **order of magnitude** of a number. This is simply the power of ten nearest to the quantity under discussion. For instance, the charge of a proton is $1.602 \times 10^{-19}\,\mathrm{C}$ to an accuracy of four significant figures, but when expressed as an order of magnitude it is simply $10^{-19}\,\mathrm{C}$. We can say that the charge of a proton is *of the order of* $10^{-19}\,\mathrm{C}$.

○ Express the following quantities to the nearest order of magnitude: the mass of the Sun $M_{Sun} = 1.989 \times 10^{30}\,\mathrm{kg}$; the radius of the Sun $R_{Sun} = 6.96 \times 10^7\,\mathrm{m}$; the constant 4π; and the Boltzmann constant $k = 8.6 \times 10^{-5}\,\mathrm{eV\,K^{-1}}$.

○ The orders of magnitude are: $10^{30}\,\mathrm{kg}$; $10^8\,\mathrm{m}$, 10^1, and $10^{-4}\,\mathrm{eV\,K^{-1}}$, respectively. (Notice that the values for R_{Sun} and k are rounded up, whilst those for M_{Sun} and 4π are rounded down.)

Using orders of magnitude can make calculations a lot simpler. For instance when multiplying (or dividing) numbers, the powers of ten are simply added (or subtracted), and this can usually be done without the use of a calculator.

⬤ What is the order of magnitude of the distance to a galaxy which has a luminosity of $L_{10} = 10^{41}$ W and a brightness of $F_{10} = 10^{-10}$ W m^{-2}?

◯ Using Equation 2.3

$$r = \sqrt{\frac{L_{10}}{4\pi F_{10}}}$$

$$= \sqrt{\frac{10^{41}\,\text{W}}{10^{1} \times 10^{-10}\,\text{W m}^{-2}}} = \sqrt{\frac{10^{41}}{10^{(1-10)}}\,\text{m}^{2}}$$

$$= \sqrt{\frac{10^{41}}{10^{-9}}\,\text{m}^{2}} = \sqrt{10^{(41+9)}\,\text{m}^{2}} = \sqrt{10^{50}\,\text{m}^{2}}$$

$$= 10^{25}\,\text{m}$$

Question 5.1 (a) Calculate the attractive electric force between an electron and a proton separated by a distance of 5.29×10^{-11} m.

(b) Compare its order of magnitude with the weight (on Earth) of a grain of sand, whose mass is of the order of 1 mg.

(Use the value $e = 1.602 \times 10^{-19}$ C for the charge of the proton. The electron's charge is $-e$. You should assume that the acceleration due to gravity on Earth is $g = 10$ m s^{-2}.) ◄

The result of that calculation is remarkable. As you saw in Block 7, Bohr had given the value $r_1 = 5.29 \times 10^{-11}$ m as the radius of the orbit of an electron in the ground state of the hydrogen atom. We know from Block 7 that such precision is not possible in the quantum world of atoms, where an electron cloud picture, showing the probability of finding an electron at a given location, is a more appropriate way of representing the position of the electron. Nevertheless, r_1 is a reasonable estimate for the separation of the electron and proton in a hydrogen atom, and in fact represents the most probable distance at which an electron may be found. The electric force between them at this separation, calculated from Coulomb's law, is of the order of 10^{-7} N, which is 1% of the weight of a grain of sand. Yet such a grain contains of the order of 10^{20} atoms. From this you can see that the gravitational force exerted by the Earth on a single atom is utterly negligible compared to the electric forces within it.

5.1.2 The fine structure constant

One aim of this section is to characterize the strength of the electrical interaction in a way that will be of universal significance, rather than simply comparing it with something else, like the weight of a grain of sand. The trouble with a value like $k_e = 8.988 \times 10^{9}$ N m^{2} C^{-2} is that it doesn't tell us, by itself, anything fundamental about the electric force. The value depends on (scientifically) irrelevant historical details, such as Napoleon defining the length of a metre by decreeing that the distance from the Equator to the North Pole should be (close to) 10 million metres. This may be convenient for airline passengers, but is not likely to be relevant to cosmology.

To characterize the strength of electric forces in atoms it is convenient to form a combination of fundamental constants that is a pure number with no units, on whose value all people will agree, whatever the system of physical units they happen to have adopted. Such a number is said to be *dimensionless*, and will characterize the strength of electric forces in a unique and universal way.

⚪ Can you think of a constant you have met earlier in this block that is dimensionless?

⚪ The constant $\pi = 3.141\,592\,654$ is dimensionless. It is defined as the circumference of a circle divided by its diameter.

Since the circumference and diameter of a circle are *distances*, they can both be measured in the same unit (say metres) and so dividing one by the other gives a dimensionless number. π has the same value whatever unit we use to measure the circumference and diameter of a circle, providing they are measured in the *same* unit.

⚪ Suppose we try to communicate our value for the Coulomb constant to an advanced civilization, elsewhere in the Universe, to see if theirs is the same as ours. There are (at least) three snags to the idea of broadcasting the bald announcement: 'Our value for the Coulomb constant is $8.988 \times 10^9 \, \text{N m}^2 \, \text{C}^{-2}$'. What do you think these are?

⚪ The recipient would need to know how the newton, metre, and coulomb, happen to have been defined. Going into the details might tell her/him/it some interesting bits of human history, but would hardly advance the cause of science.

To find a dimensionless number to characterize electrical interactions, we can proceed in two stages. The first eliminates all dependence on how the coulomb was historically defined, the second makes the result independent of the definitions of the newton and the metre.

First, we rearrange Equation 5.1 to get $F_e r^2 = -k_e Q_1 Q_2$. If we now assume that the two charged particles are an electron and a proton, with charge $-e$ and e, respectively, this equation can be written as $F_e r^2 = k_e e^2$. The product of the Coulomb constant k_e and the proton charge squared e^2 is:

$$k_e e^2 = (8.988 \times 10^9 \, \text{N m}^2 \, \text{C}^{-2}) \times (1.602 \times 10^{-19} \, \text{C})^2 = 2.307 \times 10^{-28} \, \text{N m}^2$$

Now, since (as you know from Block 5) $1 \, \text{J} = 1 \, \text{N m}$, the units N m^2 can also be written as J m.

But we have just said that $k_e e^2 = F_e r^2$, so $2.307 \times 10^{-28} \, \text{J m}$ is equal to the product of the force F_e between an electron and a proton and the square of their separation r, whatever that separation might be. So we have successfully eliminated any dependence on the coulomb — the first stage in finding the dimensionless number.

⚪ How could you express the value of such a quantity in a way that does not depend on the definition of the joule and metre?

⚪ As we explained above, if some other constant of nature could be found that also has the dimensions of energy multiplied by distance (J m), then by dividing the first quantity by that constant, the result would be a pure number with no units.

Using information about light from Block 7, we can find such a constant. The energy of a photon is given by $E_{ph} = hf$ (where h is the Planck constant and f the frequency of the wave), and the wavelength of the associated wave is $\lambda = \dfrac{c}{f}$. By multiplying the photon energy by the wavelength, the result is

$$E_{ph} \times \lambda = (hf) \times \left(\frac{c}{f}\right) = hc$$

which applies in every part of the electromagnetic spectrum. In SI units, the product of the Planck constant h and the speed of light c (to four significant figures) is

$$hc = (6.626 \times 10^{-34}\,\text{J s}) \times (2.998 \times 10^8\,\text{m s}^{-1}) = 1.986 \times 10^{-25}\,\text{J m}$$

Since both $k_e e^2$ and hc have the same SI unit (J m), it follows that the value $\dfrac{k_e e^2}{hc}$ is a pure number, whose value is quite independent of the historical circumstances underlying the definition of the joule, metre, coulomb, etc. So we have succeeded in our aim of finding a dimensionless number to characterize electrical interactions. The dimensionless number $\dfrac{k_e e^2}{hc}$ is, in fact, very similar to an important constant of atomic physics known as the **fine structure constant** (for reasons that will become apparent later). It is denoted by the symbol α_{em} (pronounced 'alpha-ee-em') and the only difference between it and the value of the constant derived above is the inclusion of the extra term '2π'. To four significant figures, the value of the fine structure constant is

$$\alpha_{em} = 2\pi \frac{k_e e^2}{hc} = \frac{2\pi \times 2.307 \times 10^{-28}\,\text{J m}}{1.986 \times 10^{-25}\,\text{J m}} = \frac{1}{137.0} \qquad (5.2)$$

The important point is that α_{em} has no units, it is dimensionless. When this number was first calculated, there was the suspicion that α_{em} might be *exactly* equal to $\frac{1}{137}$, and some effort was spent guessing the question to which the answer might be 137. However, experiment rules supreme in science, and it is now known that

$$\frac{1}{\alpha_{em}} = 137.036\,00 \pm 0.000\,01.$$

To appreciate the universal nature of this constant, imagine that a radio message has been received from an extraterrestrial civilization. After decoding, it reads as follows: 'We wish to know whether the strength of electromagnetic interactions is the same in your part of the Universe as in ours. We have determined two constants that have the same units (whose details on our planet are immaterial since we send you only the result of dividing one by the other). The first is the product of the wavelength and photon energy of electromagnetic radiation at the highest energy available to us. The second is the force between an electron and a positron, multiplied by the square of their separation. Dividing the first constant by the second, our answer is $861.022\,6 \pm 0.000\,1$. Do you agree?'

Before sending an answer, we would need to consider the following questions:

⬤ What does their 'product of the wavelength and photon energy of electromagnetic radiation at the highest energy available to us' correspond to in terms of the symbols used above?

○ This is $\lambda \times E_{ph}$ which, from above, is equal to hc. It doesn't matter that this is at a high energy, since the relationship applies right across the electromagnetic spectrum.

⬤ What does their 'force between an electron and a positron, multiplied by the square of their separation' correspond to in terms of the symbols used above?

○ This is $F_e \times r^2$ which, from above, is equal to $k_e e^2$. It doesn't matter whether the positive charge involved is a proton or a positron, since both have the same charge e.

So it seems that the extraterrestrial civilization is dealing with the same sort of things as we are.

Question 5.2   Now answer the question from the extraterrestrial civilization, does their value of $hc/k_e e^2 = 861.022\,6 \pm 0.000\,1$ correspond to our value of $1/\alpha_{em} = 137.036\,00 \pm 0.000\,01$? (*Hint:* Two experimentally determined numbers can be considered to be 'the same' if the range of values covered by the uncertainty in one number overlaps with the range of values covered by the uncertainty in the other number.) ◀

While the details of the question were clearly fictitious, the principle is an important one. As we saw in Section 2, it is a basic principle of cosmology that the same laws, with the same fundamental constants, apply throughout all regions of the Universe, at all times. The distance between the crests of an electromagnetic wave may increase, significantly, during its transit over cosmological distances and times, because of the expansion of the Universe. But at the same time the photon energy decreases in this red-shift. We assume that the product $E_{ph} \times \lambda$ was, is, and ever will be the same fundamental constant, hc, throughout the Universe. Similarly, the value for $k_e e^2$ at any point in the Universe is assumed to be the same as the value found on Earth. Different units for energy, distance, force and charge may certainly be used elsewhere in the Universe. However, dividing one quantity such as hc by another quantity such as $k_e e^2$, both of which have the unit of (energy × distance), will give a number that is independent of the actual units used. So when we calculate a dimensionless number, as for the fine structure constant of Equation 5.2, we obtain a number of universal significance, that characterizes the strength of electromagnetic interactions throughout the Universe, and on which everyone agrees.

5.2   Magnetic forces

Magnetism may be most familiar to you from the interaction of magnetic materials, such as a bar magnet and a compass needle. The magnetic properties of metals derive, however, from the motion of the electrons that they contain.

Around 1820, Hans Christian Oersted observed that an electric current flowing in a wire affects a compass needle placed close to it, thus demonstrating that the movement of charge produces a magnetic force, registered by the magnetic material in the compass needle. The converse effect is that a bar magnet exerts a magnetic force on moving charges. A dramatic demonstration (which you should *not* attempt yourself, lest it damage your equipment) is to bring a powerful magnet near to a television set, or computer screen. The current of electrons in the television tube is deflected, thereby distorting the image on the screen. To simplify the subject we can dispense with magnetic materials entirely and study the (rather feeble) forces exerted by one current on another. The simplest situation to study involves two parallel wires, carrying currents I_1 and I_2, separated by a distance r. If the currents flow in the same direction, the wires attract each other; if they flow in opposite directions, there is a repulsion (Figure 5.2). The attractive force, F_m, exerted by the entirety of one wire on a length L of the other is given by the magnetic force law

$$F_m = k_m \frac{2 I_1 I_2 L}{r} \qquad (5.3)$$

As you saw in Block 5, the SI unit of current is the ampere, abbreviated by the symbol A. It is named in honour of André Ampère who, in the 1820s, made detailed studies of the magnetic effects of current flow. One ampere is a flow of one coulomb per second: $1\,\text{A} = 1\,\text{C s}^{-1}$.

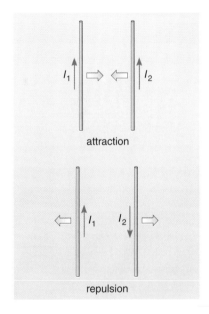

attraction

repulsion

Figure 5.2   When the currents flow in the same direction, the wires attract; when the currents are opposite, they repel each other.

Question 5.3 Show that the SI unit of k_m may be written as N A^{-2} or equivalently as $\text{N s}^2 \text{C}^{-2}$. ◄

The value of the constant k_m (which we can call the magnetic constant) is *defined* to be exactly $k_m = 1 \times 10^{-7}\,\text{N A}^{-2}$. This is because the ampere is defined to be that current which, flowing in two long parallel wires separated by a metre in empty space, produces a force of exactly $2 \times 10^{-7}\,\text{N}$ on a one-metre length of either.

Question 5.4 Suppose that a rigid horizontal metal bar carries a current of 200 A, flowing left to right. Directly above it, and parallel to it, a flexible thin wire runs between supports. The separation between the bar and the wire is 0.5 cm. When no current flows in the thin wire, it sags under its own weight. When a current of 5 A flows in it in one direction, the sag is doubled. When a current of 5 A flows in the other direction, the sag is removed. (a) In which direction is the current flowing when there is no sag? (b) What is the mass of a 10 m length of the thin wire? (*Hint*: When there is no sag, the *weight* of the wire, $F_g = mg$, must be exactly balanced by an opposing magnetic force. Assume $g = 10\,\text{m s}^{-2}$.) ◄

Magnetic forces between wires are small and so are not easily detected. To make useful technological devices, magnetic materials, such as iron, are combined with current-carrying wires to produce electric motors. But long before these devices revolutionized technology, James Clerk Maxwell made a profound theoretical prediction, without which the nature of light itself would have remained obscure. Here is a clue to his dramatic discovery.

Question 5.5 The two laws of Equations 5.1 and 5.3 involve two fundamental constants: k_e and k_m. The unit of k_e is $\text{N m}^2 \text{C}^{-2}$ and the unit of k_m is $\text{N s}^2 \text{C}^{-2}$.

(a) Calculate the value of k_e divided by k_m, and show that this result does not depend on the definition of the coulomb or the newton.

(b) What does the unit of this answer correspond to? Which constant of nature, which you have met in this course, has a unit related to this? Can you see a link between that constant and the answer in part (a)? ◄

5.3 Electromagnetic radiation

In 1873, James Clerk Maxwell (Figure 5.3) unified the laws of magnetism with those of electricity, to produce his theory of electromagnetism, with the distinctive prediction that light is a form of electromagnetic radiation. The finding of Question 5.5, that $\dfrac{k_e}{k_m} = c^2$, makes it clear, in retrospect, that light is entwined with both electricity and magnetism. However, the values of k_e and the speed of light, c, were not well determined in Maxwell's day, and this relation was a dramatic prediction of his work.

As you have just seen, Coulomb had shown that *stationary* electric charges give rise to *electric* forces. A little later, Oersted and Ampère had shown that *moving* charges (i.e. electric currents) give rise to *magnetic* forces. The next discovery in this area was made around 1830 by Michael Faraday and, independently, Joseph Henry who observed that a *changing* magnetic force produces an electric force. This phenomenon is called electromagnetic induction and is the basis of the simple dynamo, the principle of which is illustrated in Figure 5.4.

Maxwell's great contribution to the field of electricity and magnetism was to predict a further phenomenon: that a *changing* electric force produces a magnetic force. The

Figure 5.3 James Clerk Maxwell (1831–1879), was born in Edinburgh and was one of the greatest theoretical physicists of the 19th century. His 'Treatise on Electricity and Magnetism' published in 1873 explained all of the then known effects of electromagnetism and predicted the existence of 'electromagnetic waves' that travel at the speed of light. Maxwell suggested that such waves existed beyond the infrared and ultraviolet regions of the spectrum, but unfortunately didn't live to see his prediction verified in 1888 when Heinrich Hertz produced radio waves.

previous three parts of electromagnetic theory had been developed in response to experiments. There was, it seemed, no data crying out for Maxwell's fourth idea. However, Maxwell's prediction was dramatic in the extreme: according to his equations, an *electromagnetic wave* could be set up, which would travel through a vacuum (i.e. empty space) with the universal (constant) speed:

$$c = \sqrt{\frac{k_e}{k_m}} = 2.998 \times 10^8 \text{ m s}^{-1} \tag{5.4}$$

which is also the speed of light.

Waves of any frequency f were predicted to be produced when electrical charges move to and fro at this frequency. Their wavelength was then given by $\lambda = \dfrac{c}{f}$. In other words, Maxwell had not only thrown new light on light itself, but suggested the existence of electromagnetic radiation of *any* wavelength. It fell to Heinrich Hertz to provide the crucial experimental confirmation, in the late 1880s. Hertz was able to calculate the frequencies at which electrical circuits produce varying currents and to measure directly the wavelengths of the radiation produced. To within the accuracy of Hertz's data, Maxwell's prediction that

$$f\lambda = c = \sqrt{\frac{k_e}{k_m}}$$

was confirmed. Hertz also found that the familiar properties of light, involving reflection at a surface, and change of direction when passing through a prism or lens, were shown by electromagnetic waves of much longer wavelength. Guglielmo Marconi made money from these radio waves when he demonstrated them as a practical means of communication.

Maxwell's equations of electromagnetism are the basis for telecommunications, electric motors and generators, waveguides that transport electromagnetic energy, radar navigation, and a host of other things which technology has harnessed to satisfy human demands. When you next use your home computer, spare a thought for the electric and magnetic forces which guide electrons through the computer's display unit, and for the light that carries the message from the screen to your retina. Maxwell's equations describe both parts of the process.

5.4 Quantum electrodynamics

Maxwell completed his theory of electromagnetism in 1873, and you may be wondering whether that was the last word on this phenomenon. Bearing in mind what you learned in Block 7, about developments in quantum physics between 1900 and the 1920s, you will probably guess that this is not the case. The quantum physics of atoms is inextricably linked with the emission and absorption of electromagnetic radiation (photons). So clearly there was a need to unite Maxwell's theory of electromagnetism with Schrödinger's quantum model of the atom if a correct description of atoms and radiation was to be obtained.

In Block 5 we referred to another important development in physics in the early part of the 20th century, namely Einstein's theory of special relativity, which was published in 1905. A key result of this theory is that the energies of particles travelling at a substantial fraction of the speed of light, no longer obey the simple

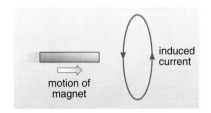

Figure 5.4 An example of electromagnetic induction. When a magnet is brought swiftly towards a loop of wire, a current is produced in the loop. The explanation is that the changing magnetic force, caused by moving the bar magnet, acts on the wire and sets up an electric force which causes electrons to move round the wire.

formula for kinetic energy that you met in Block 5. As you saw in Block 7, the Schrödinger model of the atom showed that electrons in atoms have a range of possible speeds and there is a certain probability of finding an electron with *any* speed inside an atom. For example, the most probable speed for the electron in the ground state of the hydrogen atom is around 1% of the speed of light, and even at this speed the conventional formula for kinetic energy is in error by 0.005%. At higher speeds (all of which are possible in atoms) even larger errors occur if special relativity is not taken into account.

A fully consistent explanation of the properties of atoms, electrons and radiation would therefore need to combine electromagnetism with quantum physics and special relativity, to produce what is called a relativistic quantum theory of these properties.

The first stage in this process was completed by Paul Dirac (Figure 5.5) in 1928. Dirac successfully combined special relativity with the Schrödinger model of the atom, and derived a complicated and precise formula for the energy levels of hydrogen. The differences between the predictions of his formula and the *gross* structure of the hydrogen energy levels that you read about in Block 7 show up as so-called *fine structure* in the emission lines of the hydrogen spectrum. If you were able to look closely at the lines in the hydrogen spectrum, you would see that many of them are in fact several lines very close together. Dirac's formula for the energy levels depends on the value of α_{em} and is the reason why this is known as the fine structure constant.

Dirac's work also gave a clue to how electromagnetic interactions might be modified by quantum effects. To achieve a high precision in describing tiny corrections to the Schrödinger model as a result of relativity, Dirac was forced to postulate the existence of a new particle, with the same mass as the electron, but with positive charge. We call this particle, e^+, the positron, or antielectron, and as you saw in Block 7, it was discovered in β^+-decay, shortly after Dirac's prediction. Now, when an electron and positron collide, they undergo **annihilation**, producing a pair of photons. For an annihilation at low speeds, the energy E of each photon is related to the mass m of the electron (or positron) by $E = mc^2 = 511\,\text{keV}$. Conversely, high-energy photons can create electron–positron pairs, thereby producing new particles from purely electromagnetic energy. This process is referred to as **pair creation**. The mass of an electron or positron can be expressed as $511\,\text{keV}/c^2$, so to create an electron–positron pair requires $(2 \times 511)\,\text{keV}$ or about $1\,\text{MeV}$ of energy. Pair creation therefore requires photon energies that are about 10^5 times greater than the energies of the order of $10\,\text{eV}$ involved in the energy levels of the hydrogen atom. So, at first sight, one might not need to bother about them in atomic physics. After all, the idea of energy conservation is basic to physics. Why should one need to bother about the creation of positrons, when none ever emerge from atoms, apart from the comparatively rare unstable nuclei that undergo β^+-decay?

It turns out that one should bother: the conservation of energy is something that has to work out on long time-scales; on much shorter time-scales energy accounting may be, so to speak, relaxed, provided the accounts are settled in the long run. The basic rule for this had been given by Heisenberg in the 1920s:

A failure of energy conservation by an amount ΔE may be tolerated for a time t, provided that

$$\Delta E \times t < h \qquad\qquad (5.5)$$

Figure 5.5 Paul Adrienne Maurice Dirac (1902–1984) was a British physicist who generalized the theory of quantum physics to incorporate special relativity. One of the results of his theory was that it predicted the existence of an antiparticle to the electron, which is now known as the positron.

where h is the Planck constant, 4.1×10^{-15} eV s. After this time the energy debt must be made good. This is another form of the uncertainty principle that you met in Block 7 in relation to how accurately positions and velocities of electrons in an atom can be known. It embodies a feature of the quantum world that you encountered in Block 7: whatever is allowed to happen will do so, sooner or later.

Try thinking of Equation 5.5 as an arrangement with your bank manager, who says you may go into the red by £100 for no more than 100 days, or by £1 000 for no more than 10 days, or by £10 000 for a single day. In this scenario, anything seems to be allowed, provided the product of your debt and its duration is no more than 10^4 pound-days.

● In this analogy, for what length of time could you borrow a million pounds?

○ The time is given by $\dfrac{10^4 \text{ pound-days}}{10^6 \text{ pounds}} = 0.01$ of a day, or about a quarter of an hour.

● How much could you borrow for a thousand years?

○ A thousand years corresponds to 365 000 days, so the amount you could borrow

is given by $\dfrac{10^4 \text{ pound-days}}{365\,000 \text{ days}} = 0.027$ pounds or about three pence!

In physics, the general feature of the so-called **energy–time uncertainty relation** is that you may push it to the limit: any failure, ΔE, of the conservation of energy may be tolerated for a time t, provided that Equation 5.5 holds true. The terms are not generous, but they are totally flexible, within this credit limit.

Question 5.6   To create an electron–positron pair takes about 1 MeV of energy.

(a) Suppose the pair was created out of *nothing*, what is the maximum time for which this energy may be borrowed?

(b) How could the energy debt be repaid? ◀

The energy–time uncertainty relation led to the idea that empty space, even inside an atom, is not really empty. In informal terms, it is as if electrons and positrons were constantly appearing out of nothing, and then disappearing before bank-manager Heisenberg says their credit has run out. The space inside a hydrogen atom (and inside any other atom) is filled with transient electron–positron pairs. The (negatively charged) electrons that are created are drawn towards the (positively charged) proton at the centre of the hydrogen atom. This effectively screens the charge of the proton, in a similar way to that which you met in Block 7 with regard to atoms with two bound electrons. The effect of this screening is illustrated in Figure 5.6.

Figure 5.6   (a) When measuring the force on an electron produced by a proton at large distances away, some of the proton's charge is screened by transient electron–positron pairs. (b) When measuring this force much closer to the proton, there is less screening of the proton's charge, so the effective force is increased.

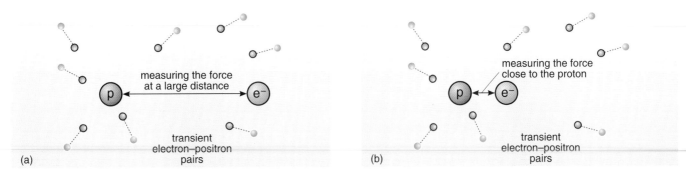

(a)

(b)

If you were to measure the electric force of attraction F_e on an electron produced by the nucleus of a hydrogen atom (i.e. a proton) when situated relatively far away from it, you would get an answer that is quantified by the fine structure constant, α_{em} of Equation 5.2. This value is the effective strength of electromagnetic interactions when screening due to transient electron–positron pairs *is included* and corresponds to the situation described by Coulomb's law (Figure 5.6a). However, if you were to measure the same effect when much closer to the nucleus, some of the transient electron–positron pairs would be further away. Consequently, there would be *less* screening, so the effective charge of the proton would appear slightly larger, and the electric force would consequently increase (Figure 5.6b). In other words, at small distances, the electromagnetic interaction will appear stronger than it does at larger distances, and so be characterized by a number that is *larger* than $\frac{1}{137}$.

The reason that the effect shows up only at short distances has to do with the finite speed of light. Effects allowed by Equation 5.5 over a short time t can increase the force only over the short distance $c \times t$, that light can travel in this time.

Question 5.7   (a) Use the result of Question 5.6 to estimate the distance scale over which the strength of the electromagnetic interaction is increased by the presence of transient electron–positron pairs in otherwise empty space.

(b) Compare this distance to the typical separation of the electron and proton in a hydrogen atom, which is of the order of 10^{-10} m. ◄

From the answer to Question 5.7 you have seen that quantum effects modify the electric force in a hydrogen atom only over distances that are about 1% of the typical separation of an electron and proton. The result is to modify the energy levels by a fractional amount that is only about 1 part in a million. Yet the discovery and explanation of such tiny effects led to the development of a whole new theory, called **quantum electrodynamics** (QED). Quantum electrodynamics is the most complete theory of electric and magnetic interactions that we possess. It incorporates descriptions of the emission and absorption of photons, and is needed to understand many features of the subatomic world. In this theory, all electric and magnetic forces are envisaged as arising from the *exchange* of photons between charged particles. Electricity, magnetism, electromagnetic radiation and the behaviour of electrons in atoms are merely different aspects of the same phenomenon. Many confirmations of this theory have now been obtained.

The final surprise of QED has already been alluded to above. It concerns how the strength of the electromagnetic interaction varies depending on the energy at which we investigate the effect. When atoms are probed in high-energy experiments, distances close to the nucleus are investigated. In these regions the strength of electromagnetic interactions is greater than the strength predicted by Coulomb's law, because shielding of the nucleus by transient electron–positron pairs is less effective. In other words, electromagnetic interactions appear *stronger* when investigated at high energies. In fact the value of α_{em} is measured to be about $\frac{1}{128}$ (or 0.007 8) at 100 GeV, as compared with its lower value of $\frac{1}{137}$ (or 0.007 3) at energies of a few eV. In later sections you will see that the varying strength of fundamental interactions with energy is a crucial feature that enables us to understand the conditions that prevailed in the early Universe.

5.5   Summary of Section 5

The electric force of attraction between charges Q_1 and Q_2, separated by a distance r, is given by Coulomb's law as

$$F_e = -k_e \frac{Q_1 Q_2}{r^2} \tag{5.1}$$

This is the force that binds electrons in atoms. Like charges repel and unlike charges attract each other.

The fine structure constant, $\alpha_{em} = \frac{1}{137}$, expresses the strength of electromagnetic interactions in a way that does not depend on any choice of units. It is a universal constant of nature.

When currents I_1 and I_2 flow in parallel wires, separated by a distance r, the magnetic force on a length L of either of the wires is given by

$$F_m = k_m \frac{2 I_1 I_2 L}{r} \tag{5.3}$$

In producing a theory that unified the phenomena of electric and magnetic forces, Maxwell predicted the existence of electromagnetic radiation that travels in empty space with speed

$$c = \sqrt{\frac{k_e}{k_m}} = 2.998 \times 10^8 \text{ m s}^{-1} \tag{5.4}$$

i.e. the speed of light.

By combining electromagnetism with special relativity and quantum physics, the theory of quantum electrodynamics (QED) was arrived at. This theory modifies Coulomb's law at very short distances, by taking account of the transient electron–positron pairs that can appear for short periods of time in empty space. These may be thought of as appearing and then rapidly disappearing, since a failure of energy conservation by an amount ΔE may be tolerated for a time t, as long as

$$\Delta E \times t < h \tag{5.5}$$

QED predicts that the strength of electromagnetic interactions increases with increasing energy, because at the short distances probed in high-energy experiments, the shielding effect of transient electron–positron pairs is less effective.

Activity 5.1   The development of a theory

This activity allows you to draw together the various strands in the origin of the theory of QED and construct a diagrammatic representation of the development of this theory. ◄

6 Strong interactions

In Block 7 you learned that there is a strong interaction, which binds quarks in nucleons (i.e. neutrons and protons). When two up quarks (u) and a down quark (d) form a proton (quark content: uud), the strong force has, largely, done its job (in much the same way that the electric force between a proton and an electron does its job, so to speak, by forming a hydrogen atom). However, there is still a residual interaction between protons and neutrons (quark content: udd), sufficient to bind them together in nuclei. This is shown in Figure 6.1a which repeats a picture first seen in Block 7. The 'left-over' part of the strong interactions of quarks is similar in nature to the left-over electromagnetic interactions between atoms that are responsible for the formation of molecules (Figure 6.1b).

Figure 6.1 (a) The strong interaction binds quarks together in nucleons. A left-over interaction binds nucleons in nuclei. (b) The electromagnetic interaction binds electrons and nuclei in atoms. A left-over interaction binds atoms in molecules.

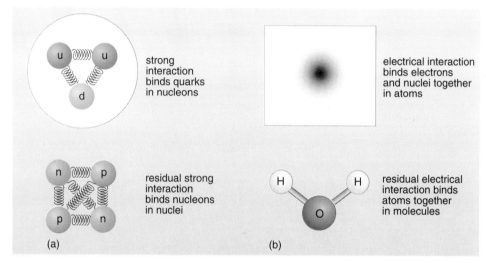

6.1 How strong is strong?

It is amazing just how strong the strong force between quarks is. At a separation of around 10^{-15} m — the typical size of a proton or neutron — the force of attraction between a pair of quarks is typically 10^5 N, which is the weight of a 10 tonne truck!

Question 6.1 (a) Use Equation 5.1 to estimate the order of magnitude of the electric force of repulsion between two up quarks separated by a distance of 10^{-15} m.
(*Hint*: Remember the electric charge of an up quark is $+\frac{2}{3}e$, where $e = 1.6 \times 10^{-19}$ C.)

(b) What fraction is this force of the strong force of attraction between the two up quarks? ◄

So the strong force of attraction between two up quarks is much larger than the electric force of repulsion between them. Most importantly, the strong force between quarks does *not* get smaller at separations larger than 10^{-15} m; it stays more or less constant, at a value of around 10^5 N. It is as if every quark were attached by an extremely strong elastic band to every other quark, or antiquark, that inhabits the same hadron (Figure 6.1a). The tension in this elastic band is the weight of a 10 tonne truck, yet it acts on a quark whose mass is thirty orders of magnitude less than such a truck.

It is this strong force that prevents quarks from being liberated in high-energy collisions. As you saw in Block 7, free quarks are *never* seen to emerge from such processes: quarks only exist confined within baryons or mesons. Consider, for example, an experiment conducted at the Large Electron–Positron (LEP) collider, at the European Laboratory for Particle Physics (CERN), near Geneva, where positrons of kinetic energy 50 GeV collide with electrons travelling in the opposite direction, with the same kinetic energy. In this case, an electron and a positron may annihilate each other, producing a quark–antiquark pair, with total energy 100 GeV or 10^{11} eV. These energies are certainly impressive: 10^{10} times greater than the 10 eV that is typical for the energy levels of the hydrogen atom. But what can such high energies achieve, against the strong force?

Question 6.2 If the force between a quark and an antiquark is of the order of 10^5 N, what is the largest separation that can be achieved with an available energy of 100 GeV? (*Hint*: Refer back to Block 5 for the relationship between work, force and distance. Use the fact that an energy of 1 eV is of the order of 10^{-19} J.) ◀

You have seen that 100 GeV of energy can separate a quark–antiquark pair by only about 100 times the size of a proton. That is as one might expect, since the mass of a proton, as you saw in Block 7, can be expressed as about 1 GeV/c^2, and therefore corresponds to an energy about 100 times less than the energy available here. The energy of the proton (1 GeV) derives from the energy of quarks confined to a region of size 10^{-15} m. Putting in a hundred times more energy (100 GeV) would allow a quark to get no more than a hundred times further away, 10^{-13} m.

● Quarks don't emerge from these collisions, so what happens to the 100 GeV that is put into the collision?

○ Energy can't be destroyed, but can only be transformed from one kind to another. In this case, the energy comes out in the form of the mass and kinetic energy of many hadrons. (Recall the proton–proton collisions, described in the 'Quarks' CD-ROM activity in Block 7, in which pions were created.)

6.2 Jets of hadrons

6.2.1 Two-branched outcomes

In the mess of debris that results from high-energy collisions between electrons and positrons, there is a tell-tale clue as to the original interaction that occurred at very short distances: it often happens that hadrons emerge as a pair of *jets* each made up of a number of hadrons. (Remember that hadrons are composite particles made of quarks.) Figure 6.2 illustrates two apparently very different outcomes from electron–positron collisions at high energies. In (a) a muon–antimuon pair is produced; in (b) a pair of jets of hadrons appears.

● What is a muon?

○ Recall from Block 7 that a muon is a fundamental particle that belongs to the class known as leptons. It is like the electron, only more massive.

In fact, the descriptions of the two basic processes in Figure 6.2a and b are comparable. They are conveniently represented by **Feynman diagrams**, named in honour of Richard Feynman (Figure 6.3), who developed them in his study of quantum electrodynamics (QED).

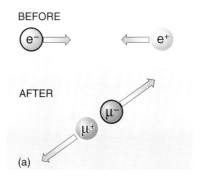

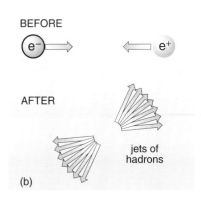

Figure 6.2 Two possible outcomes of an electron–positron collision: (a) a muon–antimuon pair; (b) a pair of jets of hadrons.

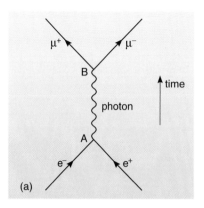
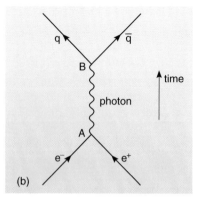

Figure 6.4 Feynman diagrams for the creation of: (a) a muon–antimuon pair; (b) a quark–antiquark pair.

Figure 6.3 Richard Phillips Feynman (1918–1988) was one of the most celebrated and colourful US physicists. He developed his own way of describing quantum processes, using what others now refer to as Feynman diagrams, which provide a simple way of tackling calculations in quantum physics. In 1986 Feynman served on the team investigating the explosion of the Challenger Space Shuttle. In his final tour de force of science communication, he laid bare the shortcomings of the Shuttle's design to a huge television audience.

Figure 6.4a illustrates a Feynman diagram description, in terms of QED, of Figure 6.2a. It is to be read from bottom to top, with the vertical direction representing the passage of time, increasing upwards. Initially the electron (e^-) and positron (e^+) are getting closer together. Their annihilation is the event labelled A. A photon is produced by the annihilation and is represented by the wavy line. In a different event, labelled B, a muon–antimuon pair is then created from the photon. From B, the muon (μ^-) and antimuon (μ^+) separate, as time progresses. Since both events A and B involve photons, they are both electromagnetic interactions. Notice that the lepton–antilepton pair that annihilate at A are the same flavour of lepton, and the lepton–antilepton pair that are created at B are also the same flavour. Leptons and antileptons are always created or annihilated as pairs of the *same* flavour in electromagnetic interactions.

The basic interaction that produces the pair of jets of Figure 6.2b is described by the Feynman diagram of Figure 6.4b. The difference is that B is now the creation of a quark–antiquark pair (of the same flavour) from the photon which was created by the electron–positron annihilation at A. As before, both of the events A and B are electromagnetic interactions. Quarks and antiquarks too are always created or annihilated as pairs of the *same* flavour in electromagnetic interactions. The difference in outcome concerns the subsequent fate of the quark (q) and antiquark ($\bar{q}$). Unlike the muon and antimuon, they cannot separate indefinitely; instead their energy is converted into jets of hadrons, in a way that is much more difficult to describe than the mere separation of a muon and antimuon.

Feynman diagrams are convenient because specific mathematical expressions can be associated with each line or intersection in the diagram. This results in formulae for calculating how often a particular outcome of a reaction occurs. Different patterns correspond to different probabilities of occurrence. We shall not worry about such calculations here, but will simply use Feynman diagrams as a tool for representing different possible reactions in a graphical way. For instance, the similarity of the Feynman diagrams in Figure 6.4a and b indicates that the probability of producing the pair of jets is given by a calculation very much like the one for producing the muon–antimuon pair.

6.2.2 Three-branched outcomes

Now, Figure 6.4a is not the whole story of what may happen in an electron–positron collision producing a muon–antimuon pair: for example, it may be that a high-energy photon is also produced. The corresponding Feynman diagram is shown in Figure 6.5. The mathematics entailed by Figure 6.5 gives a probability for radiating a photon, but the precise details of this calculation need not bother us. The important thing is that, in QED, the probability of a reaction like that shown in Figure 6.5 occurring is given by the numerical value of α_{em}. To the nearest order of magnitude α_{em} is about 0.01, so the probability of producing a photon *and* a muon–antimuon pair (Figure 6.5), rather than simply a muon–antimuon pair (Figure 6.4a), is about 1%. The fine structure constant can therefore be thought of as a measure of how often this three-branched outcome occurs as a fraction of the two-branched outcomes.

When experimenters set up detectors to find how often a muon, an antimuon, *and* a high-energy photon are produced, they find that such an outcome is about a hundred times less probable than the production of merely a muon and an antimuon, just as predicted by the theory.

⬤ Bearing in mind the conclusion of Section 5.4 that the effective strength of electromagnetic interactions increases with energy, what do you suppose happens to the chance of getting a three-branched outcome (Figure 6.5) as the collision energy is increased?

◯ The probability is given by the value of α_{em}, and the value of α_{em} increases with increasing energy, so the chance of a three-branched outcome will also increase with increasing collision energy.

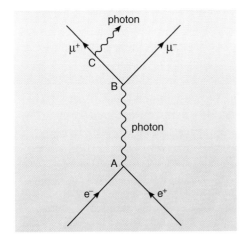

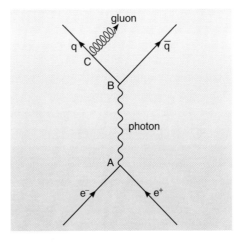

Figure 6.5 Feynman diagram for the production of a photon, along with a muon–antimuon pair.

Figure 6.6 Feynman diagram for the production of a gluon, along with a quark–antiquark pair.

Similarly Figure 6.4b is not the whole story in the production of jets of hadrons: it may happen that *three* jets are produced. The corresponding Feynman diagram is shown in Figure 6.6. It involves a quite new ingredient, called a **gluon**, represented by the curly line emerging from event C. Just as photons are the quanta of energy associated with electromagnetic interactions, so gluons are the quanta of energy whose emission and absorption is regarded as the origin of strong interactions. Unlike photons, but like quarks and antiquarks, gluons cannot escape to large distances; as a result the energy that is radiated as a gluon produces a *third* jet of hadrons. Notice that when a quark emits (or absorbs) a gluon, the quark does not change flavour. A similar thing is seen in electromagnetic interactions. When a charged lepton (such as an electron) emits (or absorbs) a photon, the lepton does not change flavour either.

Now, as we have just said, in QED the fine structure constant can be thought of as a measure of how likely it is that a three-branched outcome occurs, when compared with the chance of a two-branched outcome. Similarly, we can define a dimensionless estimate of the strength of the strong interactions on the same terms as in QED: it is simply the probability of observing a three-jet outcome (Figure 6.6), rather than a two-jet outcome (Figure 6.4b). We then no longer have to refer to extraneous things, such as the weight of a truck. The experimenters find that, with an available energy of 100 GeV, the number of three-jet outcomes (Figure 6.6) is about 10% of the number of two-jet outcomes (Figure 6.4b). So the value for this dimensionless estimate of the strength of the strong interaction, referred to as α_s, must be about 0.1. But whereas α_{em} is known to seven significant figures, the corresponding value for the strong interaction of quarks with gluons is determined much less accurately. In collisions with a total kinetic of 100 GeV, like those at the LEP collider, it is found that $\alpha_s = 0.12 \pm 0.01$.

The final ingredient in this story of jets is that, just like in QED, the strength of the strong interaction changes with the energy of the interaction. It turns out that the probability of three-jet outcomes, as a fraction of the two-jet outcomes, *decreases* with increasing energy.

⬤ What does this tell us about the strength α_s of strong interactions?

◯ Since the probability of three-jet outcomes is measured by the value of α_s, the strength of strong interactions must decrease at higher energies.

So, whereas in QED the strength of electromagnetic interactions *increases* with increasing energy, the strength of strong interactions *decreases* with increasing energy.

The corresponding values for α_s measured at different energies are shown in Figure 6.7.

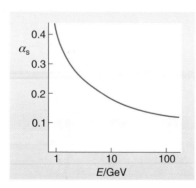

Figure 6.7 The decrease of α_s with energy, in the range from 1 GeV to 100 GeV. Note that the value $\alpha_s = 0.12$ applies at $E = 100$ GeV. At lower energies, it is considerably larger.

Question 6.3 In electron–positron collisions, the probability of producing *two* high-energy photons, along with a muon–antimuon pair, (i.e. a four-branched outcome) is smaller than that for producing merely a muon and antimuon, by a factor of the order of α_{em}^2, which is about 10^{-4}. By analogy with this situation, estimate the probability for producing four jets of hadrons, relative to that for producing only two jets, when the available energy is 100 GeV. ◀

6.3 Quantum chromodynamics

The quantum theory of the strong interactions between quarks and gluons is called **quantum chromodynamics** (QCD). Like any quantum theory it deals, not with force directly, but with the interactions between particles and quanta, represented by an event like C in Figure 6.6, where a quark emits a gluon. In quantum electrodynamics (QED) the primary interaction is of electrically charged particles with photons. In QCD there are two basic interactions: quarks (and antiquarks) interact with gluons, and gluons also interact with themselves. For example, Figure 6.8 gives two of the possible Feynman diagrams for producing four jets of hadrons, mentioned in Question 6.3. It is interactions *between* gluons that are responsible for the fact that the strength of strong interactions decreases with increasing energy.

To understand why this theory is called quantum *chromo*dynamics, you should note that 'chromo' comes from the Greek word for 'colour'. The interactions between quarks and gluons are described in terms of a new property of matter that is, rather whimsically, called **colour charge**, by analogy with conventional electric charge that you have read about throughout this course. Just as electromagnetic interactions result from 'forces' between electrically charged particles, so strong interactions result from 'forces' between colour charged particles. However, whereas conventional electric charge comes in only one type which can either be positive or negative, colour charge comes in *three* types, each of which can be 'positive' or 'negative'. These three types of colour charge are known as red, green and blue, and their opposites are antired, antigreen and antiblue. (*Note*: Colour charge has *nothing* to do with colours of light, it is merely a naming convention.) By analogy with electric charge, like colour charges repel each other, and unlike colour charges attract each other.

⬤ To what other colour charges will a particle with a red colour charge be attracted? What other colour charges will repel it?

⬤ A particle with a red colour charge will be attracted to particles with green or blue colour charge, and also to particles with antired, antigreen or antiblue colour charge. It will be repelled by particles with red colour charge.

Each quark can have any one of the three colour charges, and each antiquark can have any one of the three anticolour charges. So in effect there are three versions of each type of quark: red up quarks, blue up quarks and green up quarks, for instance. (Remember, this is in addition to the conventional electric charge that quarks and antiquarks also carry.) Gluons each carry a combination of colour *and* anticolour charge, although they have zero electric charge. Note that leptons and photons *do not* have any colour charge associated with them.

This model helps to explain many phenomena, such as why the only possible hadrons are baryons (consisting of three quarks), antibaryons (consisting of three antiquarks) and mesons (consisting of one quark and one antiquark). Each of these composite particles is *colour neutral*, that is to say it has a net colour charge of zero. Any baryon must contain one quark with a red colour charge, one quark with a green colour charge, and one quark with a blue colour charge. By analogy with conventional colours: red + green + blue = white, a neutral colour with a net colour charge of zero, as shown in Figure 6.9a.

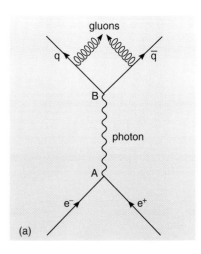

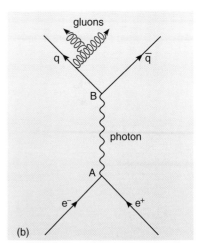

Figure 6.8 Two of the several ways for producing four jets of hadrons. In both processes, a high-energy collision between an electron and a positron produces a quark–antiquark pair. However, in (a), two gluons are radiated, one by a quark and one by an antiquark; in (b), a quark radiates a gluon, which then radiates a second gluon.

Figure 6.9 (a) Three colour charges combine to produce a net colour charge of zero (i.e. white). (b) Three anticolour charges combine to produce a net colour charge of zero (i.e. white).

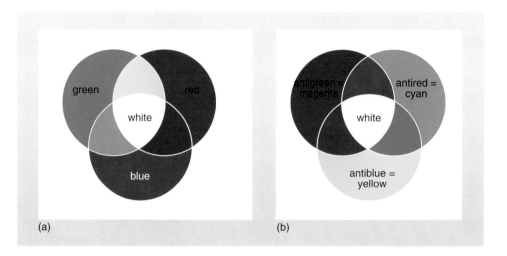

(a)　　　　　(b)

○ Can you guess what the colour charges of the three antiquarks in an antibaryon are?

○ Antibaryons must contain one antiquark with an antired colour charge, one antiquark with an antigreen colour charge, and one antiquark with an antiblue colour charge. Again this gives a net colour charge of zero, as shown in Figure 6.9b.

Similarly, the quark–antiquark pairs that constitute a meson must have the opposite colour charge to each other: red + antired = white for instance, which is a net colour charge of zero. Only particles with a net colour charge of zero are allowed to exist in an independent state, and this explains why single quarks and antiquarks are not seen in isolation. The locking up of quarks inside hadrons is referred to as **confinement**. Gluons do not have a net colour charge of zero, so they too do not escape from strong interactions. Instead, gluons will decay into quark–antiquark pairs, which in turn create further hadrons.

Question 6.4 Bearing in mind what you have learned about electromagnetic interactions, strong interactions, electric charge and colour charge, complete Table 6.1 which compares the properties of the fundamental constituents of the world around us, in terms of their electromagnetic and strong interactions. ◀

Table 6.1 The properties of the fundamental constituents of the world.

Particle	Electric charge	Colour charge	Quanta with which the particle interacts
electron	$-e$	~	photons
electron neutrino	0	-	~
up quark	$+\frac{2}{3}e$	red, green, or blue	photons, gluons
down quark	$-\frac{1}{3}e$	red, green, or blue	photons, gluons
photon	0	-	~
gluon	0	colour and anti-colour	gluons

The following points serve to compare and contrast QED and QCD.

1 In QED, photons interact with electrically charged particles and their antiparticles, but *not* directly with other photons; in QCD gluons interact with quarks and antiquarks, and *also* directly with other gluons, since all of these particles possess colour charge.

2 Photons and leptons escape from QED processes; gluons and quarks do *not* escape from QCD processes. Instead, they give rise to jets of hadrons (composite particles made of quarks) which do escape. The confinement of quarks inside hadrons results from the fact that only particles with a net colour charge of zero can exist in isolation.

3 In QED, transient electron–positron pairs cause the effective size of α_{em} to *increase* at the short distances that are probed in high-energy experiments; in QCD the interactions between gluons cause α_s to *decrease* at higher energies.

The great success of QED and QCD was to recognize that you can't have one of these differences without the other two. The self-interaction of gluons is responsible for the weakening of the strong force at higher energies, and also for confinement of quarks and gluons. Correspondingly, the fact that photons do not interact directly with other photons is related to the increasing strength of electromagnetism at higher energies, and accounts for the fact that electrons and photons emerge from atoms, in exchange for modest amounts of energy.

Thus, when we compare the strengths of electromagnetic and strong interactions, we should take account of the energy scales that are involved, and hence the associated scales of distance, bearing in mind that higher energies probe shorter distances. Even at an energy of 100 GeV though, α_{em} is still an order of magnitude smaller than the corresponding α_s of the strong interaction. But who knows what will happen at energies vastly higher than those achieved at the best laboratories on Earth? To make sense of the early Universe we need to know the answer. Fortunately the theories predict their own fates. If no new phenomenon intervenes, the strength of the QED interaction is condemned to increase with energy, while that of QCD must forever decrease. It is thus possible to estimate a rough order of magnitude for the energy at which the two theories would have comparable strengths. The answer is thought to be about 10^{15} GeV. This is a million million times greater than collision energies currently attainable in high-energy particle physics laboratories. Yet cosmologists envisage early epochs of the evolution of the Universe when such collision energies were possible.

6.4 Summary of Section 6

The strong force between quarks in hadrons is of the order of 10^5 N, at a separation of 10^{-15} m. It confines quarks to nucleons, which are approximately this size. The forces between nucleons are a left-over effect of this force, and are of correspondingly short range.

In the collisions of electrons and positrons, with total kinetic energy 100 GeV, a variety of outcomes is possible. Sometimes a muon–antimuon pair is created;

sometimes a quark–antiquark pair is created. In the latter case, the quark and antiquark cannot escape from the collision zone; instead two jets of hadrons are observed.

In collisions between electrons and positrons, the probability of radiating a high-energy photon, along with a muon–antimuon pair, is predicted by quantum electrodynamics (QED) to be of the order of α_{em}, i.e. about 1%. The probability of radiating a high-energy gluon, along with a quark–antiquark pair, is predicted by quantum chromodynamics (QCD) to be of the order of α_s, i.e. about 10%. In the latter case, the gluon cannot escape; instead a third jet of hadrons is observed.

The crucial difference between QCD and QED is that gluons interact directly with gluons, whereas photons do not interact directly with photons. This is explained in terms of both quarks and gluons possessing a so-called colour charge. There are two important consequences: quarks and gluons are not observed in isolation, and the strength of strong interactions decreases with energy. Conversely, the effective strength of QED interactions increases with energy.

These trends are expected to continue, with QCD and QED interactions becoming comparable at energies which are a million million times greater than can be studied at the present time in high-energy physics laboratories. Such huge energies are believed to have occurred in the very early Universe.

Activity 6.1 Dealing with difficult concepts

In this activity you are encouraged to use again the techniques for dealing with difficult concepts that you developed earlier in the course. ◄

Weak interactions

We now consider the second category of 'nuclear' interactions that you met in Block 7. Weak interactions manifest themselves as reactions, or decays, in which some particles may disappear, while others appear. There is no structure that is bound by a 'weak (nuclear) force', although you will often hear such a thing referred to, along with the electromagnetic force, the gravitational force and the strong (nuclear) force.

○ What form of nuclear decays are governed by weak interactions? What particle transformations take place in these decays?

○ β-decay processes (both β+- and β−-decay) are governed by weak interactions. In a β−-decay, a neutron transforms into a proton with the emission of an electron and an electron antineutrino. In a β+-decay, a proton transforms into a neutron with the emission of a positron (antielectron) and an electron neutrino.

7.1 Comparisons of fundamental interactions

As you have seen in Sections 5 and 6, electromagnetic interactions involve electrically charged leptons (e.g. the electron), quarks (all of which are electrically charged), and hence hadrons, made from quarks (e.g. a proton, p = uud). Strong interactions involve only particles that possess colour charge, namely quarks and gluons, as well as composite particles made from quarks. Neutrinos, which as you saw in Block 7 are electrically neutral leptons, are involved in neither electromagnetic interactions nor strong interactions, since they possess neither electric charge nor colour charge.

The one interaction in which neutrinos do participate is the weak interaction. The weak interactions of neutrinos from nuclear β-decays are, as the name suggests, rather feeble. A substantial amount of the energy released in a nuclear power station escapes, innocuously, as the kinetic energy of neutrinos. The vast majority of those travelling downwards pass through the Earth without interaction. However, the probability of a neutrino interacting with matter increases with the kinetic energy of the neutrino. Beams of neutrinos with kinetic energies of the order of 100 GeV are readily obtained, as decay products, at high-energy particle accelerator laboratories. At such kinetic energies, neutrinos interact as readily with a target as do electrons. For that reason, the strength of the weak interaction is recorded, in Table 7.1, as being roughly the same as that of the electromagnetic interaction.

Table 7.1 Participants, quanta, and strengths of three interactions.

Interaction	Participants	Quanta	Strength at 100 GeV
strong	colour charged particles: u, d, c, s, t, b (and their antiparticles); gluons	gluons	$\alpha_s = 10^{-1}$
electromagnetic	electrically charged particles: e^-, μ^-, τ^-; u, d, c, s, t, b (and their antiparticles)	photons	$\alpha_{em} = 10^{-2}$
weak	u, d, c, s, t, b (and their antiparticles); W^+, W^-, Z^0; e^-, μ^-, τ^-, ν_e, ν_μ, ν_τ (and their antiparticles)	W^+, W^-, Z^0	$\alpha_w = 10^{-2}$

The entries in Table 7.1 for the strong and electromagnetic interactions record what you learned in Sections 6 and 5, respectively. The key feature of these is that the electromagnetic interactions of QED involve photons, while the strong interactions of QCD involve gluons. Photons interact only with particles that are electrically charged, hence neutrinos are immune to them. Gluons interact only with particles that have colour charge, hence all leptons are immune to them. What makes weak interactions so important is that they involve all six flavours of quark (u, d, c, s, t, b), all three electrically charged leptons (e^-, μ^-, τ^-), all three neutral leptons (ν_e, ν_μ, ν_τ), and all the corresponding six antiquarks and six antileptons, that you read about in Block 7. As you will see in the next section, weak interactions enable quarks to change flavour into other quarks, and allow leptons to change flavour into other leptons.

7.2 W and Z bosons

Just as photons and gluons are involved in electromagnetic and strong interactions, respectively, so weak interactions involve other quanta, known as **W bosons** and **Z bosons**. In fact, there are two types of W boson, one with negative electric charge, the W^- boson, and one with positive electric charge, the W^+ boson. In weak interactions, W and Z bosons interact with each other, as well as with all quarks and leptons. The Universe would be an impossibly boring place without them. To see what is involved, in the simplest terms, we will consider a very few of the many interactions that are allowed by the theory of weak interactions.

As noted above, the β^--decay of a nucleus occurs when a neutron turns into a proton, with the emission of an electron and an electron antineutrino. At most, a few MeV of energy are released in this process, corresponding to the difference in mass between the original nucleus and the resultant nucleus. As you saw in the CD-ROM activity 'Quarks' in Block 7, at the quark level, the explanation is that a down quark turns into an up quark. The process is depicted by the Feynman diagram of Figure 7.1a. At event A, a down quark (d) with electric charge $-\frac{1}{3}e$ is transformed into an up quark (u) with electric charge $+\frac{2}{3}e$. A W^- boson is emitted with electric charge $-e$, thereby conserving electric charge in the process. The mass of the W^- boson is about 80 GeV/c^2, so it cannot possibly emerge from the nucleus as there are only a few MeV of energy available. However, it can exist for a very short time, consistent with the energy–time uncertainty principle, of Section 5.4. At B it produces an electron (e^-) and an electron antineutrino ($\overline{\nu}_e$), setting the energy accounts straight.

Similarly, Figure 7.1b depicts the decay of a muon (μ^-), which changes at A into a muon neutrino (ν_μ), with the emission of a W^- boson. The W^- boson then decays, at B, into an electron (e^-) and an electron antineutrino ($\overline{\nu}_e$), just as in Figure 7.1a.

In both of these weak interactions, the total number of quarks minus the total number of antiquarks is the same both before and after the interaction, i.e. one quark in the β^--decay and zero quarks in the muon decay.

The number of leptons, too is conserved. In the example of β^--decay, there are no leptons initially present, and after the interaction there is one lepton and one antilepton, a net result of zero again. As promised in Block 7, this is the explanation for why neutrinos and antineutrinos are produced in β-decays. If they were not, then the rule of lepton conservation would be violated. Notice also that the production of a charged lepton is always accompanied by the corresponding flavour of neutrino.

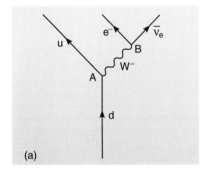

(a)

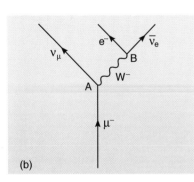

(b)

Figure 7.1 Feynman diagrams for weak interactions involving a W boson. (a) A β^--decay process, (b) the decay of a muon. Notice that W bosons are represented by a wavy line, similar to that for a photon.

● Show that the total number of leptons minus antileptons remains constant both before and after the muon decay in Figure 7.1b.

○ In the example of muon decay, before the interaction there is one lepton (the muon), after the interaction there are two leptons (the electron and the muon neutrino) and one antilepton (the electron antineutrino). This gives a net result of one lepton after the interaction, so the number remains constant.

In *all* weak interactions:

• electric charge is conserved;

• the number of quarks minus the number of antiquarks is conserved;

• the number of leptons minus the number of antileptons is conserved;

• changing the flavour of either quarks or leptons is allowed, as long as these three rules are obeyed.

Question 7.1   The antiparticle of a W^- boson is a W^+ boson, with the same mass, but the opposite electric charge. Draw a pair of Feynman diagrams showing how (a) β^+-decay, and (b) the decay of an antimuon μ^+, involve the creation and demise of a W^+ boson. In each case check that electric charge is conserved, that the number of quarks minus the number of antiquarks is conserved, and that the number of leptons minus the number of antileptons is conserved. (*Hint*: Your diagrams should be similar to those in Figure 7.1, but you will have to re-label each of the lines.) ◀

The third type of quantum involved in weak interactions is the Z^0 boson with zero electric charge. An example of the type of reaction involving the Z^0 boson is illustrated in Figure 7.2. Here a collision between an electron (e^-) and a positron (e^+) leads to the production of a muon neutrino (ν_μ) and a muon antineutrino ($\bar{\nu}_\mu$). Notice that there is one lepton and one antilepton both before and after the interaction.

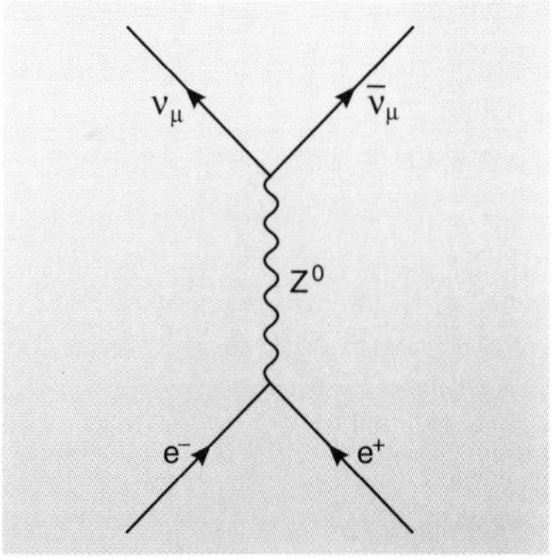

The mass of a Z^0 boson is about $90 \, \text{GeV}/c^2$. By selecting the energy of the electron and positron beams in the LEP collider to be 45 GeV each, so that the total energy of 90 GeV matched that required to create Z^0 bosons, a high rate was achieved for the production of neutrino–antineutrino pairs in the process shown in Figure 7.2. The experiment produced an important piece of information for understanding the early Universe: there are no more types of neutrino than the three already discovered and listed in Block 7: ν_e, ν_μ, ν_τ. Had there been a fourth type of neutrino, the rate of electron–positron annihilation would have been higher than that observed, by an amount significantly greater than the sensitivity of this high-precision experiment. As noted in Section 1, this was good news for cosmologists, who needed this information to calculate the rate at which nuclei were formed when the Universe was a few minutes old. Knowing that there are only three types of neutrino, cosmologists are able to compute the fraction of nucleons that survived as neutrons in (mainly) helium nuclei, a few minutes after the Big Bang.

Figure 7.2   Feynman diagram for the production of a neutrino–antineutrino pair by an electron–positron pair, thanks to the creation and demise of a Z^0 boson.

7.3   The survival of the neutron

You know from Block 7 that, apart from hydrogen, nuclei made solely of protons cannot exist. Neutrons are necessary to make massive nuclei stable, so the neutron is vital to our Universe. Without it there would be only a single element, hydrogen, making chemistry extremely drab, as it would be limited to a single type of molecule, H_2, with no one to study it.

Now the rules of strong interactions allow the construction of a neutron (udd) in the same manner as a proton (uud). Indeed, as we will show in Section 11, in the first moments of the Universe it is believed that protons and neutrons were created in *equal* numbers. Nowadays, however, the Universe as a whole contains only about one neutron for every seven protons, and the vast majority of those neutrons are locked up inside helium nuclei. Clearly then, at some stage, neutrons have 'disappeared' from the Universe. How has this happened?

The mass of a free neutron is about $1.3\,\text{MeV}/c^2$ *larger* than that of a free proton. This mass difference exceeds the mass of an electron (which is about $0.5\,\text{MeV}/c^2$) and means that free neutrons can undergo β^--decay (as shown in Figure 7.1a):

$$(\text{udd}) \longrightarrow (\text{uud}) + e^- + \bar{\nu}_e$$

This is believed to be the mechanism by which the proportion of neutrons in the Universe decreased from one in every two hadrons soon after the Big Bang, to only around one in seven today. Once neutrons are incorporated into helium nuclei they are immune from β^--decay, as helium nuclei are stable.

Yet there is still a puzzle: if free neutrons can decay into protons, how did the neutrons form helium nuclei in time to avoid the fate of decay that affects them when they are free? It was indeed a question of timing. As you will see in Section 11, the temperature of the Universe had fallen to a value that allowed the formation of helium nuclei only a couple of minutes after the Big Bang. Since a free neutron has a half-life of about 10 minutes, there were still plenty of neutrons around at this time, and all those that had not yet decayed into protons were rapidly bound up into helium nuclei. But if the half-life of the neutron were, say, only one second, there wouldn't have been many neutrons left to form nuclei a few minutes after the Big Bang. The vast majority of them would have long since decayed into protons. And one second is still a very long time, when compared to the half-life of, say, an atom in an excited state, which is more like a millionth of a second. The relatively long half-life of a free neutron is due to the fact that weak interactions (such as β^--decay) truly are weak, and therefore occur only rarely at low energies. Before attempting Question 7.2, read through Box 7.1, *x to the power y*.

Box 7.1 x to the power y

You have seen in earlier blocks that $x \times x$ can be written as x^2. Similarly $x \times x \times x$ can be written as x^3, and in fact any repeated product such as this can be written as a power. Many calculators, including the Windows calculator on your computer, have a button labelled x^y. So, to work out 2^{10} for instance, instead of having to key in 2 $\times$ 2 $\times$ 2 $\times$ 2 $\times$ 2 $\times$ 2 $\times$ 2 $\times$ 2 $\times$ 2 $\times$ 2 $=$, you can simply key in 2 x^y 1 0 $=$ and the answer is 1 024.

Negative powers can also be calculated in this way. You know that 10^{-2}, for instance, is equal to $\frac{1}{10^2}$ (Block 2 Box 7.2). Similarly any negative power, such as x^{-y}, can be written as $\frac{1}{x^y}$. So to work out 2^{-5}, for instance, you key in 2 x^y 5 $+/-$ $=$, or you key in 2 x^y 5 $=$ which will give you 2^5 and then use the $1/x$ button to get $\frac{1}{2^5}$ which is 2^{-5}. Either way, the answer is 3.125×10^{-2}.

Question 7.2   If the half-life of a free neutron were 1 s, then starting with 10^{68} neutrons (equivalent to the mass of the Galaxy) how many free neutrons would be left after (a) 30 s, (b) 3 minutes? (Remember, half the remaining neutrons will decay in every half-life that elapses.) ◀

So there is a vital condition for life as we know it: weak interactions must be truly weak at low energies. If they were as strong as electromagnetic interactions at low energies, β⁻-decay processes would happen much more readily and the half-life of a free neutron would be much shorter. As a result, the vast majority of the neutrons in the Universe would have decayed before it became possible for them to find safe havens in atomic nuclei, and there would have been no elements other than hydrogen in the Universe! Yet, at high energies, such as the 100 GeV of the LEP collider, weak interactions are comparable in strength to electromagnetic interactions, and hence only ten times weaker than strong interactions, as Table 7.1 records. How is this trick pulled off?

It turns out to result from the large masses of the W and Z bosons, which are each of the order of 100 GeV/c^2. In order for any weak interaction to occur, a W or Z boson must be created. But it is difficult to produce the massive W and Z bosons when the available energy is only 1 GeV. Consequently, at an energy of 1 GeV, where they were first investigated, weak interactions really are weak. In contrast, at an energy scale of 100 GeV, weak interactions are not so weak. At this energy, the strength of the weak interaction α_w is around 10^{-2} — the same as that of electromagnetic interactions. At this energy, W and Z bosons are easily created from the energy available. Going down two orders of magnitude in energy, from 100 GeV to 1 GeV, entails a huge decrease in the rates of weak processes. At an energy of 1 GeV, α_w is around 10^{-10}, i.e. eight orders of magnitude smaller than it is at 100 GeV.

Question 7.3   Summarize how the strengths of the three interactions that you have read about so far vary with increasing reaction energy. Be as precise as you can about their relative strengths at an energy of 1 GeV or lower, and at 100 GeV, using the information given in this and earlier sections. ◀

7.4 Summary of Section 7

Weak interactions are responsible for processes, such as β-decay, in which quarks may change flavour, and lepton–antilepton pairs may be created. They also allow leptons to change into other leptons. They involve quanta known as W bosons and Z bosons, each of which have a mass of around 100 GeV/c^2.

Weak interactions are weak only at low energies, where there is insufficient energy to create W and Z bosons easily. At an energy of 100 GeV, the strength of weak interactions is comparable to that of electromagnetic interactions, i.e. only an order of magnitude less than that of strong interactions.

Free neutrons decay into protons with a half-life of about 10 minutes; this is a weak interaction involving W bosons. The survival of some neutrons until nuclei formed in the early Universe was possible only because of the relatively long half-life of free neutrons. This is a consequence of the weakness of weak interactions at low energies, which in turn results from the large mass of the quanta involved.

8 Gravitational interactions

You may think it odd that gravitational interactions are presented last on the list of the four fundamental interactions. After all, wasn't gravity explained satisfactorily by the work of Isaac Newton in the 17th century, as we discussed in Block 3? In fact, there are two, rather distinct additions that need to be made to Newton's description of gravity. One, involving relativity, was completed by Albert Einstein in 1915. The other, involving quantum physics, has hardly begun.

8.1 Newton's gravity

The law which describes the gravitational force of attraction was discovered by Isaac Newton, around 1666.

> **Newton's law of gravity**: Two particles, separated by a distance r, attract each other with a gravitational force that is proportional to the product of their masses, and inversely proportional to the square of their separation.

Like Coulomb's law, it can be put in the form of an equation:

$$F_g = G\frac{m_1 m_2}{r^2} \tag{8.1}$$

where $G = 6.672 \times 10^{-11}\ \text{N m}^2\ \text{kg}^{-2}$ (to four significant figures) is called the constant of universal gravitation (or just the gravitational constant for short), and m_1 and m_2 are the masses of the particles. Note the close similarity with Coulomb's law, in Equation 5.1: both forces decrease with the inverse of the square of the separation, and where Coulomb's law involves the product of two charges, Newton's law involves the product of two masses. The following question compares the strengths of these two forces.

Question 8.1 (a) Calculate the gravitational force of attraction between a proton ($m_p = 1.673 \times 10^{-27}\ \text{kg}$) and an electron ($m_e = 9.110 \times 10^{-31}\ \text{kg}$) when they are separated by a distance of $5.29 \times 10^{-11}\ \text{m}$ (i.e. their typical separation in a hydrogen atom in its ground state).

(b) Compare your answer with the electric force between a proton and an electron at this separation, which you calculated in Question 5.1. ◀

As Question 8.1 demonstrates, gravity is *utterly* negligible in atomic physics. In order to quantify just how small it is, we can form a dimensionless constant to describe the strength of gravitational attractions in a similar way to that in which we characterized electromagnetic interactions.

Consider two electrons of mass m_e separated by a distance r. According to Newton there is a gravitational force of attraction between them of magnitude $F_g = G\dfrac{m_e^2}{r^2}$.

Following a similar procedure to that by which we derived α_{em} in Section 5.1, we rearrange Newton's law to get $F_g r^2 = Gm_e^2$. The product of the gravitational constant and the mass of the electron squared is:

$$Gm_e^2 = (6.672 \times 10^{-11}\ \text{N m}^2\ \text{kg}^{-2}) \times (9.110 \times 10^{-31}\ \text{kg})^2 = 5.537 \times 10^{-71}\ \text{N m}^2$$

From Section 5.1, you know that another constant with the unit of $N\,m^2$ (or equivalently $J\,m$) is hc. Earlier we calculated:

$$hc = (6.626 \times 10^{-34}\,J\,s) \times (2.998 \times 10^8\,m\,s^{-1}) = 1.986 \times 10^{-25}\,J\,m$$

So dividing one constant by the other, with the value of 2π thrown in for good measure to match the similar expression for α_{em}, gives

$$\alpha_g = 2\pi \frac{Gm_e^2}{hc} = \frac{2\pi \times 5.537 \times 10^{-71}\,N\,m^2}{1.986 \times 10^{-25}\,J\,m} = 1.752 \times 10^{-45} \tag{8.2}$$

We have therefore calculated a dimensionless measure of the strength of the gravitational interaction, α_g. Its value is a number so small that it is impossible to imagine. Comparing the value of α_g (about 10^{-45}) with that of α_{em} (about 10^{-2}), shows that gravitational forces are around 43 orders of magnitude smaller than electric forces, at the level of individual electrons.

Gravity comes into its own only when there are large aggregates of particles, feeling no other force. The strong and weak interactions of nuclei have very short ranges, so they make no contribution to the force between, say, an apple and the Earth. But why should gravitational forces dominate in this situation instead of electric forces?

⬤ Does the gravitational force act over larger distances than the electric force?

◯ No, Equations 5.1 and 8.1 show that both gravitational and electric forces act over large distances with the *same* kind of inverse square law, i.e. they are proportional to $\frac{1}{r^2}$.

⬤ Do the electric forces cancel out somehow?

◯ Yes, electric forces can be attractive *or* repulsive because objects can possess either positive or negative electric charge, and like charges repel whilst unlike charges attract. Gravitational forces are *always* attractive — there is no such thing as a repulsive gravitational force. The reason for this is that mass only comes in one form — 'negative mass' and 'antigravity' remain in the realm of science fiction.

So, the reason that gravity dominates the interaction between an apple and the Earth is that they are both electrically neutral, to very high accuracy. In order for the electric force of repulsion between an apple and the Earth to be similar to the gravitational force of attraction between them, only 1 atom in every 10^{20} would have to be ionized. We owe the downwards fall of the apple to the fact that matter is electrically neutral to an accuracy far better than 1 part in 10^{20}.

As a consequence of gravity, therefore, objects near to the surface of the Earth possess a property that we refer to as *weight*. The weight of an object is defined as the magnitude of the force of gravity acting on that object. In other words, the weight of an object of mass m_1 at the surface of the Earth is given by Equation 8.1, when we set m_2 equal to the mass of the Earth, and r equal to its radius. As you know from Block 5, the weight of an object of mass m_1 is also given by

$$F_g = m_1 g \tag{8.3}$$

where g is the acceleration due to gravity at the surface of the Earth, about $9.8\,m\,s^{-2}$.

Question 8.2   Combine Equations 8.1 and 8.3 to calculate the mass of the Earth. (Assume that the radius of the Earth $r_{Earth} = 6.4 \times 10^6$ m, the gravitational constant $G = 6.7 \times 10^{-11}$ N m^2 kg^{-2} and the acceleration due to gravity at the Earth's surface $g = 9.8$ m s^{-2}.) ◀

8.2 General relativity

In the period between 1905 and 1915, Albert Einstein wrestled with the consequences of another feature of gravity, which had been crystal clear since the time of Newton: you cannot use the motion of an apple, under gravity alone, to weigh that apple.

That remarkable fact bears closer examination. On Earth, a 100 g apple has a weight of about 1.0 N, while one of half the mass, 50 g, has a weight of only 0.5 N. However, the two apples fall in almost the same manner, and would do so in exactly the same manner, were it not for the force of air resistance. In a vacuum, it is impossible to determine whether a hammer weighs more or less than a feather, merely by watching them fall, since they do so with the same acceleration, quantified by the value g near the surface of the Earth.

The reason for this is that weight is directly proportional to mass, $F_g \propto m$. Doubling the mass, m, of an object also doubles its weight, i.e. the gravitational force F_g acting on it. The acceleration has the same value, $g = \dfrac{F_g}{m}$ and hence tells us *nothing* about either the weight or the mass! Most of us take this fact implicitly for granted, but there is really no reason why weight and mass should necessarily be related in this manner. In case you're wondering how you can ever measure the mass or weight of an object, weighing machines all involve a force additional to gravity, such as that provided by the springs inside a set of bathroom scales. This enables us to measure the weight of an object by balancing two opposing forces, i.e. gravity and the spring force in a set of bathroom scales. Most such machines have a scale that indicates the mass of the object, which again implicitly assumes a direct proportionality between weight and mass, and also that you are using the weighing machine at the surface of the Earth!

To avoid the complications which the concept of weight involves, Einstein eventually chose to dispense with the idea of gravitational force entirely. Since everything falls with the same acceleration, he decided that it was better to think about the regions of space and time in which this acceleration occurs. He forgot about whether there happens to be a feather or a hammer there, since it makes no difference which is present. So he had a difficult job: to do everything that Newton had done, but without using the idea of force, and then to see if this resulted in a new prediction.

Here is not the place to describe how he went about that. Suffice it to say that he was brilliantly successful, in a mission that few had even contemplated. Einstein's theory of **general relativity** reproduced all the old results of Newton, but without even thinking about weight. In addition, using the new theory, he went on to explain small departures in the motion of the planet Mercury from what was predicted by Newton. He was also able to predict the effects of the Earth and Sun on light, something that had been quite impossible using the idea of weight, since there is no meaning to the weight or mass of a photon. He predicted that light from a distant star would be deflected, when it passes close to the Sun, en route to us (see Figure 8.1). This was first detected during a solar eclipse, in May 1919, and has since been confirmed on many occasions to a high level of accuracy.

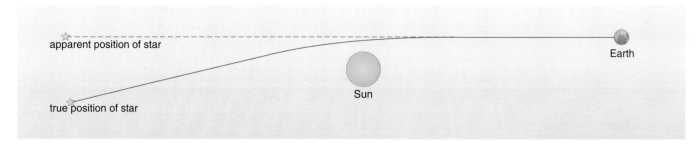

apparent position of star

Earth

Sun

true position of star

Another prediction of general relativity is that accelerating massive objects will radiate **gravitational radiation**, which propagates through space as a wave, in much the same way that accelerating charged particles radiate electromagnetic radiation. There is excellent (indirect) evidence that massive objects, such as pairs of stars orbiting around each other in close proximity, do indeed radiate gravitational energy. In 1974, American astronomers Joe Taylor and Russell Hulce discovered a remarkable system: two neutron stars orbiting around each other once every eight hours. (Neutron stars are collapsed, dead stars with a mass comparable to that of the Sun, but only of the order of 10 km across; they have densities comparable to that of an atomic nucleus.) As this star system was monitored over several years, it was discovered that the eight-hour orbital period was changing very slightly: the period becomes shorter by 75 μs every year. This implies that the system is losing energy. But where is the energy going to? The answer is that the system is steadily giving off gravitational radiation. Calculations showed that the rate of energy loss by gravitational radiation predicted by general relativity agrees exactly with the measured changes in the orbital period of the two neutron stars.

Despite the many confirmations of general relativity, actually *detecting* gravitational radiation on Earth is an enormous challenge that is currently being tackled in a variety of ambitious experiments. It is likely that during the lifetime of this course you will read that these searches for gravitational radiation are beginning to bear fruit.

Figure 8.1 The deflection of light by the Sun (not to scale). The angle by which light is deflected, for a star that is seen exactly at the edge of the Sun, is only about 0.000 5°.

8.3   Quantum gravity

The final remarkable feature of gravity is that no one has yet figured out a convincing way of combining quantum physics with general relativity. It is a sad irony that 80 years after Einstein's great work we still do not have a proper relativistic quantum theory of gravity, usually referred to simply as a theory of **quantum gravity**. Einstein made important contributions to quantum physics by explaining the photoelectric effect (Block 7) and he also invented relativity. If anyone deserved to discover a relativistic quantum theory of gravity, it was he. The reasons that we still haven't got one are twofold.

First, there is practically no experimental data on the interplay of gravity and quantum physics, because gravity is so weak at the level of individual particles. The second problem is a conceptual one. You have seen that the quantum physics of atoms involves uncertain speeds and positions for the electrons (Block 7 Section 3). In a quantum theory of gravity, somehow the notions of space and time themselves would have to become uncertain. In non-gravitational quantum physics one is not sure of exactly what one will measure, here and now, or there and then. In a quantum theory of gravity, one would be unsure of what here and now, or there and then, might mean!

Despite these difficulties, it is believed that quanta of gravitational energy exist. They are known as **gravitons** and have zero electric charge and zero mass. It is predicted that gravitons interact with everything: not just material bodies with mass, but also photons and gluons, which have no mass, and neutrinos, whose masses (if any) are as yet unknown. Moreover, gravitons are predicted to interact with other gravitons. That makes photons the unique quanta that do not interact directly with themselves.

While the history of science is full of examples of experiment leading theory, as in the early days of quantum physics, or theory leading experiment, as in the case of the work of Newton, Maxwell and Einstein, it is rare to be stymied on both fronts. This has increased both the humility and determination of scientists. Recent scientific literature abounds with speculative ideas about what a quantum theory of gravity might involve, one of which will be mentioned, very briefly, in Section 10. The difficulty of imagining what a quantum theory of 'fuzzy' space and time might be will set a limit to how far back we can trace the history of our Universe.

Question 8.3   Summing up the differences between Coulomb's law and modern QED theory, one might say the following: 'Coulomb's law was phrased in terms of a force between electrically charged particles. Modern QED theory describes electromagnetic interactions in terms of the exchange of photons.' Write a similar pair of sentences to describe the differences between Newton's law of gravity and what a quantum theory of gravity might involve. ◀

8.4   Summary of Sections 5–8

Having arrived at the conclusion that gravitational interactions do not fit so well into the pattern of description of the three other interactions, we can update Table 7.1, as Table 8.1.

Table 8.1   Participants, quanta and strengths of four interactions.

Interaction	Participants	Quanta	Strength at 100 GeV
strong	colour charged particles	gluons	$\alpha_s = 10^{-1}$
electromagnetic	electrically charged particles	photons	$\alpha_{em} = 10^{-2}$
weak	quarks, leptons, W bosons, Z bosons	W bosons, Z bosons	$\alpha_w = 10^{-2}$
gravitational	everything	gravitons	$\alpha_g = 10^{-45}$

In conclusion, we may group the descriptions of all four interactions under a variety of headings:

1   *Quanta*: Strong interactions involve gluons; electromagnetic interactions involve photons; weak interactions involve W^+, W^- and Z^0 bosons; gravitational interactions involve gravitons, though evidence for the latter is hard to come by.

2   *Range*: Electromagnetic and gravitational interactions have a large range, and both forces decrease with the inverse square of distance. Electromagnetic energy is radiated by accelerating charges, and propagates through space as an electromagnetic wave. Gravitational energy is radiated by accelerating massive

objects, and propagates through space as a gravitational wave. Both the strong and weak interactions have a very small range, comparable to the size of individual nuclei.

3   *Theories*: Strong, electromagnetic and weak interactions are well described by relativistic quantum theories. The first to be developed was quantum electrodynamics (QED), for electromagnetic interactions. This involved combining quantum physics with special relativity and the inclusion of phenomena such as transient electron–positron pairs. Quantum chromodynamics (QCD) describes the strong interaction in a comparable way, with the key difference that the exchanged quanta, called gluons, interact with themselves, as well as with quarks. This results in the permanent confinement of quarks and gluons within hadrons, and means that quarks and gluons have never been observed in isolation. The theory of the weak interactions also involves mutually interacting quanta, W and Z bosons. Gravity awaits a 'marriage' with quantum physics.

4   *Participants*: Only quarks participate in strong interactions, quarks and charged leptons participate in electromagnetic interactions, all quarks and all leptons participate in gravitational and weak interactions.

5   *Strength*: As indicated in Table 8.1, the strong, electromagnetic and weak interactions have strengths that differ only by an order of magnitude at energies of 100 GeV. As befits its name, the strong interaction is stronger than the other two. The weak interaction is very weak at low energies, where there is a big price to pay for exchanging its massive quanta. However, at energies around 100 GeV, the comparability of strength with electromagnetic interactions becomes apparent. Again gravity stands out on a limb, due to its almost indescribable weakness, at the level of individual particles. This makes it hard to get good data on the interplay of gravity and quantum physics. It is also hard to get good ideas about what such a theory would entail, since it must somehow incorporate a 'fuzziness' of space and time.

In Section 10, these interactions will be discussed further, to see if some of the differences between them might be less important than at first appears. The conclusions will have further consequences for the evolving Universe of Section 11.

But first, we take an interlude from the main story of the block to see how all four interactions work together, for our good, in the Sun.

9 Four forces in the Sun

In the preceding sections you have seen how all processes in the Universe may be described in terms of four fundamental interactions. In order to consolidate your understanding of these interactions, this section looks in turn at the way in which they each operate in a relatively nearby part of the Universe — the Sun. Ultimately, it is these four interactions that are responsible for the light and other electromagnetic radiation produced by the Sun, without which life on Earth would be impossible. But here on the Earth, the only information that scientists can obtain about the Sun comes from the electromagnetic radiation and the neutrinos that it emits. A video at the end of this section will show you how these emissions are studied. You will see how scientists use such observations to infer what is happening deep inside the Sun, and so relate its behaviour back to the four fundamental interactions that lie at the heart of all universal processes.

9.1 Gravitational interactions in the Sun

As you saw in Block 3, the Sun is a ball of gas, consisting mostly of hydrogen and helium atoms, with slight traces of other, more massive elements. It has a radius of about 7×10^8 m and a mass of about 2×10^{30} kg. That's over 100 times the radius of the Earth, and over 300 000 times its mass. The large mass inside the Sun exerts a huge gravitational force on the outer layers, pulling them towards the centre. However, the Sun's radius does not appear to be changing by any great amount, so the Sun must be in an equilibrium state: the gravitational force (acting inwards) is exactly balanced by the pressure of the gas (acting outwards). It has been calculated that the pressure at the centre of the Sun is about 200 billion times the atmospheric pressure at the surface of the Earth.

When the Sun formed, it contracted under the influence of gravity from a much larger and more diffuse cloud of gas. As it did so, gravitational energy was converted into internal energy of the gas, and the result was that the temperature in the centre became very high indeed. So high in fact that nuclear fusion was initiated, and it is this process (discussed below) that maintains the high temperature and pressure in the core of the Sun today. The temperature at the centre of the Sun has been estimated at about 14 million kelvin.

The high temperature implies that the particles have high kinetic energies — a few keV would be a typical value. The speeds of the electrons and protons in the centre of the Sun, corresponding to this kinetic energy, are around 30 000 km s^{-1} and 700 km s^{-1}, respectively.

⬤ Why do the electrons and protons have such different speeds?

○ The electrons are much less massive than the protons. Since they have the same kinetic energy, the electrons must be moving faster. (Remember, $E_k = \frac{1}{2}mv^2$)

At such a high temperature, the hydrogen and helium atoms collide with such huge kinetic energies that they are completely ionized. The electrons are stripped away from the nuclei giving rise to a gas of electrons and positively charged nuclei. Furthermore, the extreme pressure implies that the density at the centre of the Sun is also extremely high — about 150 times that of water — and so the electrons and nuclei are very close together. This high density of electrons and nuclei, all moving around extremely fast, provides just the conditions under which there is a high chance of a nuclear reaction taking place.

9.2 Strong and weak interactions in the Sun

As you saw at the end of Block 5, nuclear energy can provide immense amounts of power. In nuclear power stations the source of this power is nuclear fission — splitting massive nuclei apart into smaller components to release energy. In the Sun, the opposite processes — nuclear fusion — occurs, in which light nuclei become bound together into more massive ones, again with the release of energy. The process of energy generation by nuclear fusion is the process that sets stars apart from other objects in the Universe. It's what defines a star to be a star.

The most abundant particles in the centre of the Sun are electrons, hydrogen nuclei and helium nuclei, and it is the hydrogen nuclei — protons — that first concern us. Under normal, Earth-bound conditions, if two protons approach close to one another they are repelled by an electric force, since both particles have a positive electric charge e. Under the conditions of extreme temperature and pressure at the centre of the Sun, however, the kinetic energy of some of the protons is great enough that they can approach close enough to each other for the strong interaction to bind them together before they are repelled by their similar electrical charge. It should be noted, though, that the chance of any particular proton reacting with another proton is extremely rare — on average an individual proton will have to wait for more than 10^{10} years before such a reaction happens! (This is just as well, or the Sun would have burnt itself out long ago.) But two protons alone do not constitute a stable nucleus (as you saw in Block 7 'Nucleons and nuclei' CD-ROM Activity 5.1). To maintain stability, one of the protons transforms into a neutron, leading to the overall reaction:

Step 1:

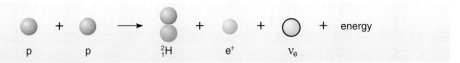

In this reaction, two protons interact to produce a nucleus of 'heavy hydrogen' (known as deuterium), a positron and an electron neutrino. The nucleus of deuterium is simply a proton and a neutron bound together. The net effect is that one of the original protons has been converted into a neutron, with the emission of a positron and a neutrino. It is these two particles which largely carry away the energy released by the reaction, as kinetic energy. This is identical to the process of β^+-decay that you met in Block 7. As you saw there, at a deeper level this process may be understood as the conversion of an up quark into a down quark, since a proton has the quark composition (uud), whilst a neutron has the composition (udd).

○ How may this process be understood in terms of the transfer of a W boson?

○ As you saw in Figure 7.3a in the answer to Question 7.1, an up quark can transform into a down quark with the emission of a W^+ boson. The W^+ boson then decays into a positron and an electron neutrino.

Since the process involves W bosons, it depends on the weak interaction. Without this, the whole process of energy release in the Sun could not even begin. So Step 1 involves *both* the strong interaction *and* the weak interaction; the strong interaction binds the two protons together and the weak interaction is responsible for conversion of a proton to a neutron.

The deuterium nucleus created in Step 1 is then able quickly to capture another proton in a process that relies on the strong interaction again overcoming the electric force of repulsion between two positively charged particles. This reaction forms a nucleus of the light isotope of helium (helium-3), with the emission of a γ-ray photon which carries away some energy:

Step 2:

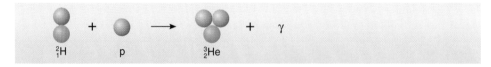

At this stage, two possibilities arise. The helium-3 nucleus can either combine with another helium-3 nucleus, or with a helium-4 nucleus. (The material from which the Sun formed contained roughly one helium-4 nucleus for every 12 hydrogen nuclei.) However, about 86% of the helium-3 nuclei follow the first route and in this case the reaction may be represented by:

Step 3:

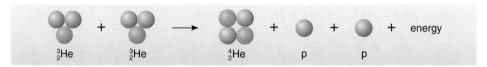

In this reaction, which relies on the strong interaction yet again, two helium-3 nuclei combine to form a helium-4 nucleus, with the emission of a pair of protons. The protons carry away the energy released in this reaction as kinetic energy.

The second route, in which nuclei of helium-3 and helium-4 interact, involves the creation and demise of nuclei of lithium, beryllium and boron along the way. The net result of the process, as far as nuclei are concerned, is that two helium-4 nuclei are formed at the end of it — the one that went in, as it were, and a newly created one. As a result of weak interactions, electron neutrinos are also produced in these other reactions, with energies that are different from the neutrinos produced in Step 1. The detection of these neutrinos with a range of energies provides one of the most sensitive tracers of the processes deep within the Sun, as you will see in Activity 9.1.

⬤ What is the overall result of the process described in Steps 1 to 3 above?

◯ Three protons are required to make each helium-3 nucleus (Steps 1 and 2), and then two helium-3 nuclei are required to create a helium-4 nucleus and release two protons (Step 3). In total, six protons give rise to a nucleus of helium-4, and two protons are released, along with two positrons, two electron neutrinos, and γ-ray photons.

Whichever route is followed, the overall process involves the conversion of four hydrogen nuclei (protons) into a single helium-4 nucleus — a sequence often referred to as the proton–proton chain. Let us now examine the implications of energy conservation in this process, particularly in Step 3. You know that mass and energy are interchangeable, as expressed by Einstein's famous formula $E = mc^2$. For this reason, as you saw in Block 7 Section 5, it is often convenient to express the masses of subatomic particles in units of GeV/c^2. The mass of a helium-3 nucleus is $2.808\,GeV/c^2$, whereas the mass of a helium-4 nucleus is $3.727\,GeV/c^2$ and the mass of a proton is $0.938\,GeV/c^2$. So, in Step 3 of the reaction chain discussed above, for instance, a mass of $(2 \times 2.808\,GeV/c^2) = 5.616\,GeV/c^2$ 'goes in' but a mass of only $3.727\,GeV/c^2 + (2 \times 0.938\,GeV/c^2) = 5.603\,GeV/c^2$ appears in the products. There is an apparent mass loss of $0.013\,GeV/c^2$, or $13\,MeV/c^2$ — where has this gone to? As you know, mass and energy are interconvertible, and energy cannot be created or destroyed, merely transformed from one form to another (including mass). In fact, this $13\,MeV/c^2$ of 'missing' mass appears as an extra $13\,MeV$ of kinetic energy of the reaction products.

Question 9.1   As mentioned above, the overall reaction process involves four protons which are converted into a single nucleus of helium-4. Using the data given above, what is the difference in mass between four protons and one helium nucleus? Where does this difference in mass go to? ◀

Question 9.2   (a) Which of the three steps in the above reaction chain depend on the weak interaction, and why?

(b) Which of the three steps depend on the strong interaction, and why? ◀

The energy released as a result of nuclear fusion reactions appears mostly in the kinetic energy of the reaction products. This means that the particles in the core of the Sun move faster, and faster means hotter. One effect of the nuclear fusion reactions is therefore to maintain the high temperatures in the centre of the Sun. Without this source of energy, the Sun would collapse under the influence of gravity.

Nuclear fusion reactions only occur within the central 2% of the Sun's volume. This is a region about 400 000 km in diameter that contains roughly 60% of the Sun's mass. Only here are the conditions of temperature and density high enough to overcome the mutual repulsion between protons due to their electric charge. The next stage of the story is to follow the fate of the energy that is produced in the core of the Sun, as that energy is transported to the surface.

9.3   Electromagnetic interactions in the Sun

Energy transport within the Sun occurs principally by two methods: convection and radiation. Convective energy transport refers to processes in which hotter material is transported to regions further from the centre that are cooler. Radiative energy transport is the transport of energy in the form of photons from deep within the Sun. Figure 9.1 shows the regions of the Sun in which different processes occur, and the different zones are discussed in turn in the following sections.

9.3.1   Radiative energy transport

The dominant process for energy transport within most of the Sun's interior is radiation. This process relies on electromagnetic interactions: the interaction between matter (chiefly electrons) and photons.

⬤   In Block 7 you saw how atoms are able to emit and absorb photons. What can you recall about how these processes operate?

Figure 9.1 A cut-away model of the Sun showing the core, in which energy is liberated by nuclear fusion, the radiative zone, the convective zone, and the photosphere.

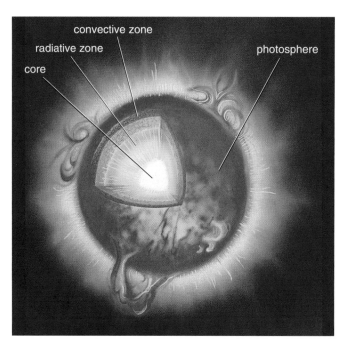

When an atom makes a transition from one state to another of lower energy, the energy lost by the atom is carried away by a photon in a process known as *emission*. To make atoms jump to states of higher energy, photons of the correct energies must be supplied. The energy gained by the atom is exactly equal to that supplied by the photon, in a process known as *absorption*.

Further processes will be discussed below, involving free electrons as well as electrons bound to nuclei, but all of these processes are types of electromagnetic interaction, because they involve photons. For all but the outer layers of the Sun, the temperature is such that the atoms are completely ionized — the electrons and nuclei are not bound together but are free to move about independently. The kinetic energy possessed by the electrons and nuclei comes from the energy liberated by the nuclear fusion reactions that have just been described. The process by which this kinetic energy is first converted into radiation is known as *free–free emission* (because the electron is 'free' both before and after emitting the photon), and is illustrated in Figure 9.2. Whenever a high energy (negatively charged) electron and a (positively charged) nucleus encounter one another, they will experience an electric force of attraction. The path of the electron will change, and in the process it will accelerate — both its speed and direction of motion will change. As you know from Block 7, the energy of the electron has two components — kinetic energy due to its speed of motion and electrical energy associated with its position in relation to the nucleus. Initially the electron will speed up as it approaches the nucleus, but on travelling away again will slow down to a speed less than that which it initially possessed. As in any process, energy is conserved, and the net result here is that the electron loses energy which appears in the form of a photon. Therefore an electron accelerating in the vicinity of a nucleus will emit radiation.

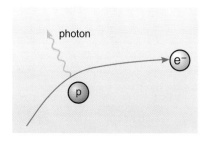

Figure 9.2 The process of free–free emission. An electron passing close to a nucleus will accelerate and in the process will emit a photon.

At the temperatures that exist near to the centre of the Sun, the speeds of the particles are such that most of the photons produced by the free–free emission process will be X-ray photons with energies of a few tens of keV. Consequently, the 25 MeV of energy liberated by *each* reaction to produce a helium-4 nucleus, imparts kinetic energy to the electrons and nuclei, and then in turn provides enough energy for the production of maybe a thousand X-ray photons. Once these X-ray photons have been produced, you may think that they would simply stream out of the Sun. However, it's not quite as simple as that.

There are plenty of obstacles in the way of a photon on its way from the core to the surface of the Sun, and in fact the energy released in the centre has been estimated to take several million years to reach the surface!

The first important process by which photons are impeded on their journey to the surface is known as *electron scattering*. This process can be visualized as a collision between two particles. As illustrated in Figure 9.3, when a high-energy photon encounters a free electron, the direction of the photon will change, and so will its energy. In general, the photon will lose energy and the electron will gain energy in this process.

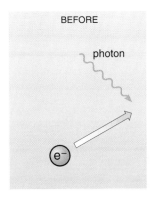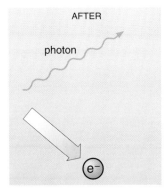

Figure 9.3 Scattering of photons by electrons. When a photon encounters a free electron, its direction and energy will change. In general, the photon will lose energy (i.e. its wavelength will increase) and the electron will gain energy in this process.

Although these interactions proceed very rapidly, the densities in the radiative zone of the Sun are so high that a photon typically travels only about 0.1 mm between each scattering event. Since each scattering changes the direction of the photon, and removes some energy, the net effect is twofold. As shown in Figure 9.4, it takes the photon a long time to get anywhere, and by the time it has travelled outwards from the centre by an appreciable distance, its energy has substantially decreased.

Another important process by which photons interact with electrons is that of absorption. In the radiative zone of the Sun, free electrons can absorb photons, in a process known as *free–free absorption*. The photon disappears and its energy is transferred directly to the electron. Remember from Block 7 Section 2 that free electrons do not have energy levels, so can absorb or emit energy in any amounts. This process may be seen as the inverse of the free–free emission process described earlier.

In the outer parts of the radiative zone, temperatures, densities and pressures are all reduced somewhat. The result is that not all the nuclei are ionized, and hydrogen and helium *atoms* are present in ever increasing quantities. When photons are absorbed by atoms, they again disappear with the result that the atom as a whole gains energy. This process, which you met in Block 7, is often referred to as *bound–bound absorption* because the electrons remain bound to the atom both before and after the event. In extreme cases, again as you saw in Block 7, if the absorbed photon has high enough energy, an electron is ejected from the atom, carrying away some of the photon's energy, in a process known as *ionization*. This is also sometimes referred to as *bound–free absorption*, again describing the initial and final states of the electron. Absorption processes involving bound electrons are illustrated schematically in Figure 9.5a and b.

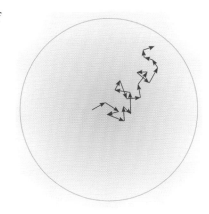

Figure 9.4 The so-called 'random walk' of a photon travelling through the Sun. Each change in direction is the result of the photon scattering off an electron.

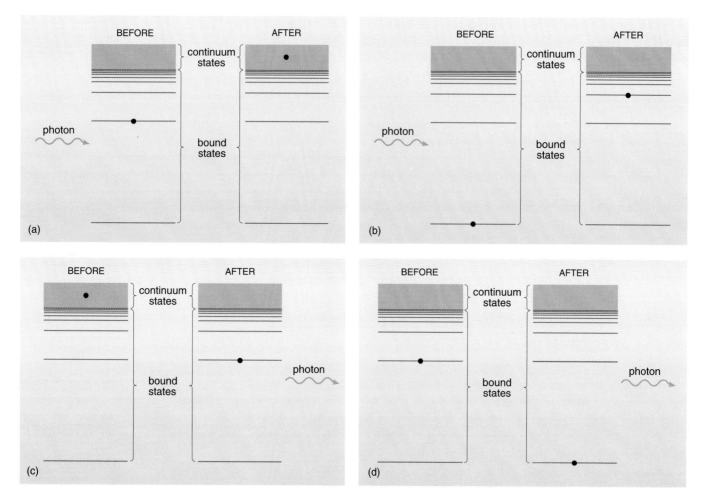

Figure 9.5 Absorption and emission processes that involve bound electrons. The energy levels shown are those of a hydrogen atom. When the atom has a particular value of energy, corresponding to a certain energy level, the energy level is marked with a dot. A continuum state corresponds to a separated proton and electron, so an electron in these states is described as 'free'. The processes are: (a) bound–free absorption, (b) bound–bound absorption, (c) free–bound emission, and (d) bound–bound emission.

An electron with sufficient energy can subsequently re-emit a photon. The process of free–free emission has already been described above. Two other ways in which a photon may be emitted are *free–bound emission* and *bound–bound emission* (see Figure 9.5c and d). In the first of these, a free electron becomes bound to a nucleus. During this *recombination* process, which is the opposite of ionization, the excess energy of the electron is carried away by a photon. The second process of photon emission is when an atom makes a transition from one quantum state to a new quantum state with a lower energy such that the atom loses energy (you met this process in Block 7). Each decrease in energy is accompanied by the emission of a photon, and the energy of the photon that is emitted will be equal to the energy difference between two atomic energy levels.

Question 9.3 In the process of free–free emission (Figure 9.2), an electron accelerates when passing close to a nucleus, and emits a photon whose energy corresponds to the change in energy of the electron. In the process of bound–bound emission (Figure 9.5d), which you also met in Block 7, the atom makes a transition from one quantum state to another with the consequent emission of a photon.

(a) How will the allowed values of energies of the emitted photons compare in these two cases?

(b) When the results of a large number of these emission processes are examined, what will the spectra of the emitted photons look like in each case? ◄

As noted earlier, the scattering, absorption and emission processes described above mean that it takes a long time for radiation to transport energy away from the core. The zone of radiative energy transport within the Sun, throughout which these processes occur, extends from the core to within only 100 000 km of the surface (i.e. it encompasses about 86% of the radius, see Figure 9.1). Beyond this point, convection becomes the more important mode of energy transport.

9.3.2 Convective energy transport

You met the idea of convection in Block 2 in the context of the Earth's atmosphere.

○ What force is responsible for driving this mode of energy transport?

○ The force of gravity is responsible, since convection relies on regions that are 'lighter' rising above other regions that are 'heavier'.

Within the convective zone of the Sun (Figure 9.1), temperatures are cool enough (a few hundred thousand degrees) for many neutral atoms to exist. Since these atoms can absorb photons, they impede the passage of radiation from below and, moving from the centre outwards, the temperature suddenly falls much more quickly. This is believed to be the trigger for convection, but the exact mechanisms operating in the Sun are still poorly understood.

Broadly speaking, as the gas in the convective zone of the Sun is heated from below, pockets of it become hotter, and so expand. These pockets are less dense than those immediately surrounding or overlying them, and so rise due to buoyancy in much the same way as a hot-air balloon is able to rise. As the less dense pockets of gas rise, cooler pockets fall to take their place. On rising to the top of the convective zone, the hot gas cools again, falls to the bottom of the convective zone, and so the cycle repeats. In this way, energy is transported from the lower layers of the convective zone to the higher layers within the Sun.

9.3.3 Energy transport in the photosphere

The overall effect of the processes of emission, absorption, scattering and convection is that photons gradually diffuse outwards from the centre of the Sun, losing energy as they do so. In this way, the energy of the original photons is continually recycled through countless absorption and emission events.

○ How many photons of visible radiation with energy around 2.5 eV would result from a single X-ray photon of energy 25 keV?

○ Energy is not created or destroyed, merely transformed. So an energy of 25 keV is sufficient to create $\dfrac{25\,000\,\text{eV}}{2.5\,\text{eV per photon}} = 10^4$ photons of visible radiation.

So, a single X-ray photon produced in the core of the Sun may give rise to many tens of thousands of photons of visible radiation by the time the energy has been transported to the outer layers of the Sun. Eventually though, these photons of light emerge from the 'surface' of the Sun — a region known as the photosphere (Figure 9.1).

The photosphere sits on top of the convective region of the Sun, and is a region where radiative transport of energy once again dominates. Within the photosphere, the temperature of the Sun falls from about 6 000 K, just above the convective zone, to about 4 000 K at its top. The photosphere represents the region above which the Sun is transparent to radiation, no more absorption events take place above this. It is a region only about 500 km thick, but from which almost all the energy emitted by the Sun is radiated away into space. From the time it leaves the photosphere, a photon takes about eight minutes to travel to the Earth, bounce off the page in front of you, enter your eye and create an electrical response on your retina.

The light that is emitted from the solar photosphere has a continuous spectrum of radiation with a characteristic black-body shape. At higher levels in the photosphere, the lower temperatures enable the atoms to absorb photons of certain wavelengths. The overall visible spectrum of the Sun, shown in Figure 9.6, is therefore a black-body continuum corresponding to a temperature of about 6 000 K, with absorption lines superimposed on top of it. These lines of the absorption spectrum enable astronomers to determine the detailed chemical composition and physical state of the photosphere — the only part of the Sun's body that can be observed directly. As you saw in Block 7, it was the detection of previously unknown absorption lines in the Sun's spectrum that led to the discovery of the element helium, in the 19th century.

Figure 9.6 The solar spectrum.

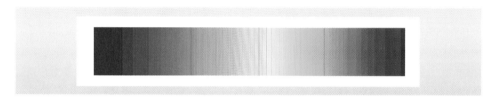

Another clue to the behaviour of the Sun is that small regions of the solar photosphere that are a few thousand kilometres in diameter are seen to regularly rise and fall with a period of about five minutes. Astronomers think that these vertical oscillations are caused by low-frequency seismic waves, generated by turbulence in the convective zone, moving outwards through the Sun's atmosphere. The study of these phenomena is known as **helioseismology**, and you will find out more about it, and what it tells us about the processes deep within the Sun, in the following activity.

Activity 9.1 Seeing inside the Sun

You should now watch the video 'Seeing inside the Sun'. ◀

9.4 Summary of Section 9

Gravity is responsible for initiating the huge temperatures, pressures and densities that exist in the core of the Sun. Such conditions are necessary in order for nuclear fusion to occur.

The strong interaction allows hydrogen nuclei to fuse together, ultimately to make helium nuclei. In the first stage of the process, the formation of a deuterium nucleus, the weak interaction is responsible for the conversion of a proton into a neutron.

The mass of a nucleus of helium-4 is somewhat less than the mass of the four hydrogen nuclei (protons) from which it is built. This 'lost' mass appears in the form of photons and increased kinetic energy of the reaction products, according to $E = mc^2$.

The neutrinos emitted by these fusion reactions can be detected on Earth. By studying solar neutrinos, scientists hope to discover whether neutrinos change from one flavour to another, and so determine whether neutrinos possess mass.

High-energy electrons undergo free–free emission processes, releasing more photons. The photons scatter from electrons, losing energy and changing direction with each interaction. Photons may be absorbed by free electrons or by atoms, and atoms or free electrons may spontaneously emit photons. The net result is that photons gradually diffuse out of the Sun.

The photons emerging from the photosphere of the Sun have a continuous spectrum that is characteristic of a black body at a temperature of about 6 000 K. Superimposed on top of this are absorption lines caused by elements present within the photosphere of the Sun.

Helioseismology is the study of solar oscillations caused by seismic waves originating deep within the Sun. This technique is used to determine how the temperature and density varies throughout the Sun's interior.

10 Unified theories

The tally of interactions was completed in Sections 5–8. According to current reckoning there are *no more than* four fundamental interactions of all matter and radiation: strong, electromagnetic, weak and gravitational. Great interest, among physicists and cosmologists, attaches to the question: are these four interactions really so distinct, or might they be different facets of some more basic unity of nature?

The idea of unifying descriptions of force is not new: you saw in Section 5.3 that Maxwell achieved a spectacular unification of electricity, magnetism and light. Recently there has been much activity in investigating a scheme for the unification, at high energies, of weak interactions with electromagnetism. This is the subject of Section 10.1, on *electroweak unification*. The consequences will be tested by particle accelerators that are currently under construction, or at the planning stage, and some answers may be known by the time you read this.

Emboldened by this activity, some theorists have suggested a unification of the electroweak theory with QCD, the theory of the strong interaction. This is the subject of Section 10.2, on the so-called *grand unification*. Testable predictions are harder to come by, here. Perhaps the Universe itself is our best laboratory.

So as not to leave gravity out of the fold of a unified quantum theory, attempts have been made at what is called *superunification*, which is mentioned briefly in Section 10.3. Such ideas are highly speculative, but may give a clue to the nature of the very early Universe. A schematic picture for this idea of unification is shown in Figure 10.1, which we shall revisit over the next few sections.

Figure 10.1 A schematic illustration of the unification processes that will be discussed in Section 10. At low energies the four fundamental interactions appear to be quite distinct, but at progressively higher energies they become unified.

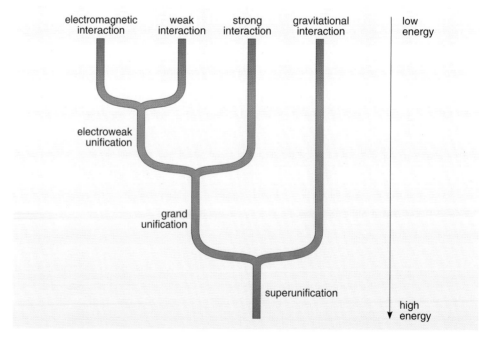

Please note that Sections 10.1–10.3 are designed to give merely the flavour of enterprises that are the subject of intense current research. Unlike previous parts of the block, they contain matters on which there is no clear consensus. Nevertheless, the questions are likely to endure. Also note that the word 'unification' is used in an *active* sense. This section is not about armchair discussions, as to whether things are different or similar. It involves real questions about the behaviour of quarks and leptons, at very high energies, and hence it will figure in our account of the history of the Universe in Section 11.

A loose analogy may help. Suppose you are given three substances, at room temperature: A is a solid, B is a liquid, C is a gas. The substances are clearly different, in crucial respects. No amount of words or thought will make them into the same thing. But if you raise the temperature, so that A melts, you may discover that, as liquids, A and B have close similarities, which were unsuspected at room temperature. That might lead you to a 'unified theory of AB liquids'. Increasing the temperature further, so that both A and B evaporate, you might find strong similarities between A, B and C as gases, and hence formulate a 'unified theory of ABC gases'. It's a *little* like that with, respectively, the weak, electromagnetic, and strong interactions.

The significance for cosmology is that there was, almost certainly, an early hot epoch of the Universe when weak and electromagnetic interactions were more unified than now appears. There was probably an even earlier, hotter, epoch when electroweak interactions and strong interactions may have been unified. If so, radically new processes, that turn quarks into leptons, and vice versa, may have been in operation, leading to a possible explanation of features of the currently observable, far cooler Universe.

10.1 Electroweak unification

You know, from Section 7, that the large masses of the W and Z bosons are responsible for the long half-life of the neutron, and the very feeble interactions of low-energy neutrinos from nuclear β-decay. The similarity in strength of electromagnetic and weak interactions becomes apparent when comparing the interactions of electrons and neutrinos with kinetic energies of the order of 100 GeV, or greater; well below that energy, there is gross disparity.

A mechanism to explain the high-energy **electroweak unification**, and the lower-energy difference, was proposed in 1964 by a number of theorists. The name of one of them, Peter Higgs, has become attached to a new particle, the **Higgs boson**, on whose existence the proposal relies. In the mid-1990s, construction began on a new particle accelerator, the Large Hadron Collider (LHC) at CERN, near Geneva, shown in Figure 1.2. On this machine, and its recently upgraded neighbour, the Large Electron–Positron collider mark 2 (LEP2), ride the hopes of discovering the Higgs boson, or some new surprise instead.

Just why the Higgs boson should exist is a complicated tale, but the following discussion will give you the general idea. A unified electroweak theory must be able to account for all three quanta involved in the weak interaction (W^+, W^- and Z^0 bosons) as well as the photon that is involved in the electromagnetic interaction. The problem is that the W and Z bosons have mass and interact with each other, whereas photons are massless and do not interact with other photons. Photons cannot have mass, otherwise there would be no such thing as Coulomb's law. Massive quanta — such as the W and Z bosons — cannot produce an inverse square law of force; their effects decrease much faster with distance. The problem then is one of developing a theory which explains the existence of four quanta, three of which are different from the other one.

According to the current theory of electroweak unification, there are four so-called 'Higgs fields', one corresponding to each of the W^+, W^- and Z^0 bosons and the photon. Three of these fields 'give mass' to the W and Z bosons. The fourth field does not give mass to the photon, but will be detectable as a true particle — the Higgs boson — with a mass of around $1\,000\,GeV/c^2$. Therefore, at an energy scale of around $1\,000\,GeV$, the electromagnetic and weak interactions will appear truly unified and merely be different aspects of a single electroweak interaction.

⬤ Which location on Figure 10.1 corresponds to this energy?

◯ It is where the branches representing the electromagnetic and weak interactions join together. Write the value of this energy on Figure 10.1 at the appropriate place.

As you can see, the story of the Higgs boson is a somewhat tangled tale. Nevertheless, it is good science: to get a satisfactory explanation of effects at energies currently available (about $100\,GeV$), theorists have been led to predictions at not much higher energy (about $1\,000\,GeV$). This outline has been given because it is probable that during the lifetime of this course you will read in the newspapers one or other of the following types of headline: either (a) 'physicists delighted: Higgs boson found'; or (b) 'puzzle for physicists: where is the Higgs boson?'

The issue of electroweak unification is important for cosmology: what hope do we have of charting the story of the Universe back to times when the energies were enormously higher than $1\,000\,GeV$, if there is a problem in the region between $100\,GeV$ and $1\,000\,GeV$?

Table 10.1 Quanta involved in electroweak unification.

Quanta	Mass/$\dfrac{GeV}{c^2}$
photon	
W^+ boson	
W^- boson	
Z^0 boson	
Higgs boson	

Question 10.1 (a) Using information from above and from Section 7, complete Table 10.1 to summarize information about the masses of the quanta involved in electroweak unification.

(b) What is different about photons when compared with the W and Z bosons, and what consequences does this have? ◀

10.2 Grand unification

Confirmation of the details of electroweak unification will still leave the strong and gravitational interactions out of the unified fold. Further unification of the forces of nature is an obvious theoretical challenge.

As already mentioned, the strength of the electromagnetic interactions of QED *increases*, rather slowly, with the energy transfer involved in the process. The corresponding measure of the strength of the strong interactions of QCD *decreases* with the energy transfer, again rather slowly. This raises an interesting pair of questions: at what energy scale might they become equal; and might there be new processes at this energy scale, expressing a **grand unification** of strong and electroweak interactions, leaving only gravity out of the fold?

The answer to the first question is rather sobering: the proposed energy scale for grand unification is about eleven orders of magnitude higher than can be achieved with even the planned new particle accelerators. As noted in Section 6.3, it is of the order of $10^{15}\,GeV$, as compared with the energies of the order of $10^4\,GeV$ that will be available at the Large Hadron Collider when it is completed in 2005. Such very high energies were probably involved in the early Universe, but they will not be achieved, by human means, on Earth, for the foreseeable future. At this energy it is predicted that there is a single interaction, characterized by a single strength. The strength of interactions in this *Grand Unified Theory* (GUT) is estimated to be around $\alpha_{GUT} = \frac{1}{42}$ at an energy of 10^{15} GeV.

Which location on Figure 10.1 corresponds to this energy?

It is where the branches representing the electroweak and strong interactions join together. Write the value of this energy on Figure 10.1 at the appropriate place.

The answer to the second question 'What new processes might occur at this energy?' is rather intriguing. The expectation is that there are quite new interactions, involving bosons with masses of the order of 10^{15} GeV/c^2. Let's call such hypothetical particles **X bosons**, because we know nothing about them, directly, from experiment. The prediction is that these new interactions allow quarks to change into leptons, matter into antimatter, and vice versa in each case.

A Grand Unified Theory will have new Feynman diagrams that express these new quantum possibilities; some examples are shown in Figure 10.2. The reason that we have not yet seen such processes working at energies far below 10^{15} GeV is analogous to the slowness of neutron decay. Remember that weak interactions, responsible for neutron decay, involve W and Z bosons and are indeed very weak at energies far smaller than the 100 GeV that corresponds to the mass of the W and Z bosons. Processes involving X bosons would similarly be very weak at energies far smaller than the corresponding 10^{15} GeV that corresponds to the mass of an X boson, and would be incredibly slow at the energies that are currently observable (between about 100 GeV and 1 000 GeV). While the behaviour of the hot early Universe would depend crucially on the processes mediated by X bosons, what we observe at lower energies hardly depends on them at all.

However, the new processes *might* show up, very rarely, at lower (i.e. achievable) energies. For example, one effect of such new processes may be that protons are not stable, but decay, with an enormously long half-life. The proton half-life predicted by the Grand Unified Theory is of the order of 10^{33} years; this is immensely longer than the age of the Universe, which is (only) of the order of 10^{10} years.

So how might one detect proton decay, in a reasonable time, say, of one year?

Here the intrinsically random nature of all subatomic processes helps: starting with 10^{33} protons (equivalent to a mass of over a thousand tonnes) and waiting for a few years, it might be possible to observe a few decays.

Experiments approaching this sensitivity are currently in progress, and might bear fruit within the lifetime of this course.

Question 10.2 (a) How many orders of magnitude of energy transfer have you explored in this course, from the study of atomic processes to the quest for a Higgs boson?

(b) How many orders of magnitude are there between the highest energies we can study on Earth and those that might be entailed by grand unification? ◀

Even if evidence in support of grand unification emerges from searches for rare processes, such as proton decay, or (as sometimes happens in science) from less expected quarters, one step will remain in the ambitious attempt to construct a coherent 'theory of everything': the construction of a theory of quantum gravity.

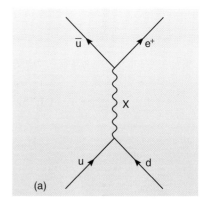

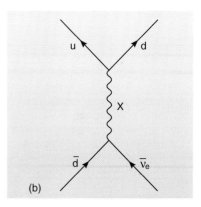

Figure 10.2 Some Feynman diagrams illustrating the types of new process that might occur at energies above 10^{15} GeV. (a) An up quark and a down quark react together to form an X boson, which then decays into an antiup quark and a positron. (b) An antidown quark and an electron antineutrino react together to form an X boson, which then decays into an up quark and a down quark.

10.3 Superunification

As already discussed, in Section 8, Einstein transformed the Newtonian theory of gravity as a force into a reinterpretation of space and time. His theory of general relativity entailed no quantum physics, though it profoundly modified ideas of space and time. Two of the obstacles to combining it with quantum physics have been mentioned: the difficulty of introducing probabilistic ideas into the discussion of the properties of space and time themselves; and the lack of laboratory data against which to test such attempts.

Nevertheless, human ingenuity is proverbial. A current aspirant to a theory of quantum gravity involves the descriptions of particles as *strings*, rather than points. Differences between such string theories and previous quantum theories are apparent only on tiny scales of distance, typically of the order of 10^{-34} m, i.e. 10^{19} times smaller than a proton. At present, such ideas attract some of the most fertile minds of our age, at an intellectual frontier. Whether they lead to testable predictions remains to be seen. One hope is that the difficulty of achieving **superunification**, of all four interactions, results from there being only one way of doing it, which we have not yet found. If a theory for superunification is found, it might predict the types and masses of particles, such as the hypothetical X bosons of grand unification. It might even explain why there are six flavours of quark, six flavours of lepton, and four types of electroweak boson.

In order to see at what scales of mass and energy superunification may be relevant, it is instructive to define a mass and an energy based on the universal constants that apply to gravitation (G), relativity (c), and quantum physics (h). Since these three constants characterize the Universe in which we live, the mass and energy scales derived in terms of these constants must also characterize our Universe. The universal constant of gravitation is $G = 6.7 \times 10^{-11}$ N m^2 kg^{-2}; the speed of light is $c = 3.0 \times 10^8$ m s^{-1}; and the Planck constant is $h = 6.6 \times 10^{-34}$ J s. From these three constants, it is possible to form a quantity with the unit of mass. It is known as the Planck mass and is defined by

$$M_{Pl} = \sqrt{\frac{hc}{2\pi G}} \tag{10.1}$$

The Planck energy is then given by:

$$E_{Pl} = M_{Pl}c^2 \tag{10.2}$$

This gives an estimate of the energy scale at which relativistic quantum physics and gravity become inextricably entwined. It is imagined that superunification occurs at such an energy.

Question 10.3   (a) Evaluate the Planck mass, in kilograms.

(b) Evaluate the Planck energy in joules, and then convert its value into electronvolts. (Remember 1 eV = 1.6×10^{-19} J.)

(c) By how many orders of magnitude does the likely energy for superunification exceed that for grand unification? ◄

○ Which location on Figure 10.1 corresponds to the Planck energy calculated in Question 10.3?

○ It is where the branches representing the grand unified interaction and gravitational interaction join together. Write the value of the Planck energy on Figure 10.1 at the appropriate place.

It is at this scale of energy, some 16 orders of magnitude higher than the energies that have been studied on Earth, that the standard model for the history of the Universe will begin, in the next section. Ultimately, one might hope to derive the entire evolution of the Universe, from the Planck scale of superunification, at 10^{28} eV, through the X boson scale of grand unification, around 10^{24} eV, down to the Higgs boson scale of electroweak unification, now under intensive experimental investigation at 10^{12} eV on planet Earth, and from thence through the well-charted territory of Sections 5–7, right down to the 2 eV photons that carry this message to you. Whether or not an understanding of all 28 orders of magnitude lies within the compass of the human intellect, only time will tell. In either case, it is a glorious project.

Question 10.4   What name is used to describe each of the new types of 'particle' predicted by: (a) electroweak unification, (b) grand unification, (c) current ideas regarding superunification? ◄

10.4 Summary of Section 10

Electroweak unification has been accomplished, on paper, by a theoretical device for giving mass to the W^+, W^- and Z^0 bosons, while leaving the photon massless. A consequence is the prediction of a new potentially observable particle: a Higgs boson with a mass of around 1 000 GeV/c^2. At the time of writing (1998) this particle is being hunted with great tenacity. If it is found, that will be remarkable confirmation of theory; if it is ruled out, that will be a remarkable triumph of experiment. In either case, our understanding of the early Universe will increase.

Extrapolating the observed decrease of α_s and the observed increase of α_{em}, over the well-charted territory up to 100 GeV, one may guess that grand unification of electroweak and strong interactions occurs at around 10^{15} GeV. Grand unification is expected to entail X bosons that cause proton decay, at a very slow rate, which may be observable on Earth.

The Planck energy of 10^{19} GeV appears to set a fundamental limit on particle energies at the first instant of creation. At such an energy, a theory of quantum gravity is needed, in which the properties of space and time are as indeterminate as those of matter. Such a superunified theory is being sought. One candidate treats particles as strings, rather than points.

11 The evolving Universe

In this section we shall describe the standard model for the evolution of the Universe, from the distant past to the present day. Although there is little experimental evidence for some of the processes described in this section, the ideas presented are the best explanation we have for the reasons why the Universe has the structure, contents and behaviour that we observe today. There are two components to study — this text and a CD-ROM activity entitled 'A history of the Universe'. As noted in the Study Guide, you may study these two components in a variety of ways.

Activity 11.1 A history of the Universe

In this activity we have provided you with an interactive tour of the history of the Universe. Using it you will be able to examine any of the epochs that are described in this section, and investigate the processes occurring at that time, or you can choose to interrogate the CD-ROM to look at a particular process and find out over what periods of time it was important. This CD-ROM is intended to be used in a way which is unlike any you have met so far in this course. The Study File notes give further details. ◀

11.1 Time, space, temperature and energy

The conventional view of the Universe is that, at the very instant of the Big Bang, the Universe came into being. There was no 'before' this instant since the Big Bang marked the creation of time. No location for this event can be specified since the Big Bang marked the creation of space. All that can be discussed are times after the Big Bang, and things that happen in the space created as a result of it. This is a difficult concept to visualize; but please bear with us and examine the consequences that follow.

Question 11.1 (a) What were the conclusions of Sections 2 and 3 about how the separations between distant objects, and the temperature of the Universe, vary with time?

(b) What does this imply about conditions in the early Universe? ◀

The thread running through this section is therefore one of a Universe in which space is forever expanding, and in which the temperature is forever falling. In the early part of its history, every time the Universe increased in age by a factor of one hundred, it also cooled by a factor of ten and distances within the Universe increased by a factor of ten.

⬤ When the Universe was 1 s old, its temperature was 10^{10} K. What was the temperature of the Universe when it was (a) 100 s old, and (b) 10^4 s old?

◯ (a) As the Universe aged from 1 s to 100 s (a factor of one hundred increase in age), so its temperature fell by a factor of ten from 10^{10} K to 10^9 K. (b) As it aged by another factor of one hundred from 100 s to 10^4 s, its temperature fell by another factor of ten from 10^9 K to 10^8 K.

The fact that the separations between objects increase only by a factor of ten for every factor of one hundred increase in the age of the Universe, actually means that the expansion rate is slowing down. For instance, two objects that were (say) 10^5 km apart when the Universe was 1 s old would be 10^6 km apart when the Universe was 100 s old, and 10^7 km apart after 10^4 s.

○ What is the mean speed of recession of one of the objects referred to above, as measured from the other object, (a) when the Universe is between $1\,s$ and $100\,s$ old and (b) when it is between $100\,s$ and $10^4\,s$ old?

○ (a) You know that speed $= \dfrac{\text{distance}}{\text{time}}$, and that over the interval between $1\,s$ and $100\,s$, the separation increases from $10^5\,km$ to $10^6\,km$. Therefore the mean speed of recession over this interval is given by:

$$\frac{(10^6\ km - 10^5\ km)}{(100\,s - 1\,s)} = \frac{9 \times 10^5\ km}{99\,s} = 9\,000\ km\,s^{-1}$$

(b) In the interval between $100\,s$ and $10^4\,s$, the separation increases at a mean rate of

$$\frac{(10^7\ km - 10^6\ km)}{(10^4\,s - 100\,s)} = \frac{9 \times 10^6\ km}{9\,900\,s} = 900\ km\,s^{-1}$$

So even though distances between objects increase by the same factor (i.e. ten) for every hundredfold increase in time, the expansion rate of the Universe (as given by the speed of recession) actually decreases with time. The expansion rate continues to decrease at later times. As mentioned in Section 2, this contributes to the decrease in the value of the Hubble constant with time, and is due to the gravitational attraction between all the matter in the Universe. The effect is referred to as deceleration (Section 2.5.1).

Although the rate of cooling and expansion has changed somewhat since these early times, the overall trend still continues. A consequence of the cooling and expansion is that the mean energy per particle (i.e. the energy available for any reaction to occur) is continually reduced. This has important implications for the ways in which the four fundamental interactions manifest themselves at different epochs.

In Sections 5 to 8 you saw that the four fundamental interactions have very different strengths and act on different types of particle. Then, in Section 10, you saw the clue to their unification, namely that the strengths of the interactions vary with the energy of their environment. Furthermore, at very high energies, particles can transform into different types — quarks into leptons for instance. So the fact that only quarks feel the strong interaction whilst leptons do not, is irrelevant at very high energies. Figure 11.1, which is an annotated version of Figure 10.1, shows that at higher and higher energies, first the electromagnetic and weak interactions become unified as energies reach around $1\,000\ GeV$. Then the strong interaction becomes unified with the electroweak interaction at an energy of around $10^{15}\ GeV$. Finally, at the very highest energies of at least $10^{19}\ GeV$, gravity too may become unified with all the other interactions.

At the very earliest times, the Universe was extremely hot, the mean energy available per particle was extremely high, and so the unification of interactions discussed in Section 10 would have occurred naturally. As the Universe has cooled, the available energy has fallen, and the interactions have in turn become distinct until the current situation is reached in which four different interactions are observed. The relationship between the mean energy of a particle, the temperature of the Universe, and the time at which such energies and temperatures applied, is shown in Figure 11.2.

You will appreciate from Figure 11.2 that the rest of Section 11 will necessarily refer to incredibly small times after the Big Bang (notice how far along the graph 1 second

Figure 11.1 The unification of the four fundamental interactions as energy increases towards the bottom of the diagram. As the Universe has aged, so the mean energy of each particle has fallen, and the various interactions have become distinct from one another as the energy has fallen below the thresholds shown. The approximate ages of the Universe when each of these interactions became distinct are also shown.

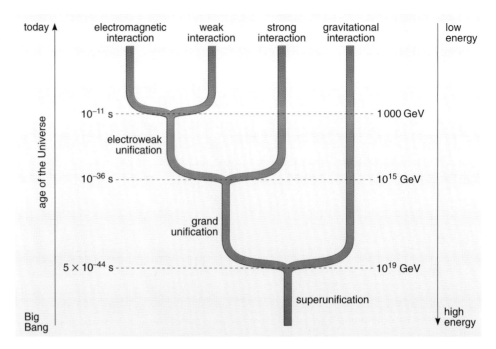

appears). Many important processes took place when the Universe was significantly less than 1 s old, when the energy available for processes in the Universe was extremely high. In fact, most of the important processes were completed by the time the Universe was only a few minutes old! It is impossible to imagine a time as short as (say) 10^{-36} s, and you shouldn't attempt to try. However, you will need to be comfortable with manipulating large negative and positive powers of ten throughout the rest of this section. Return to Activity 1.2, if necessary, to revise this topic. You should also read Box 11.1, *Orders of magnitude revisted*. For each of the intervals under discussion in Sections 11.2 to 11.7 (and shown in Figure 11.2) the time, temperature and energy ranges are given. As you read through these sections you can imagine yourself travelling down the line of the graph in Figure 11.2.

Figure 11.2 The mean energy per particle and the temperature of the Universe at different times in its history. The divisions of this graph are described in Sections 11.2–11.7. Notice that the axes are shown on powers-of-ten scales to accommodate the vast ranges of energy, temperature and time that are necessary. You will find it useful to refer back to Figures 11.1 and 11.2 as each successive stage in the history of the Universe is introduced.

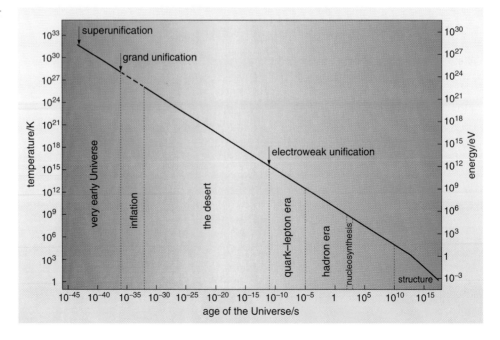

Box 11.1 Orders of magnitude revisited

When discussing ideas in cosmology — the study of the Universe as a whole — many quantities are not known very accurately and it is often appropriate to express them to the nearest order of magnitude. As you saw in Box 5.1, this can have the added bonus of making many calculations a lot simpler.

In this section, we shall refer to the age, temperature and energy scale of the Universe at various stages in its history. Here it is appropriate to use numbers that are *slightly* more accurate than simple orders of magnitude. To see why this is the case, think about what might be meant by the phrase 'the number midway between 10^5 and 10^6'. At first sight you may think the answer is 5×10^5. However, since we're dealing with orders of magnitude here, a more appropriate answer is $10^{5.5}$. But what does it mean to express ten to the power five and a half? Here is not the time or place to enter a discussion of non-whole number powers of ten, but if you have a calculator with a button on it labelled 'x^y', then key in ⑴ ⓪ x^y ⑤ ⚫ ⑤ ⚌ and see what answer you get. (You may use the Windows calculator on your computer if you wish.)

The answer is 3×10^5 (to one significant figure). So, when dealing with orders of magnitude, the mid-point between 10^5 and 10^6 is $10^{5.5}$ which is equivalent to 3×10^5.

● Determine the mid-points between the following pairs of orders of magnitude: 10^8 and 10^9; 10^{-4} and 10^{-3}.

○ $10^{8.5} = 3 \times 10^8$; $10^{-3.5} = 3 \times 10^{-4}$.

This is a useful concept for Section 11 because of a few numerical coincidences: the number of seconds in a year is about 3×10^7 or $10^{7.5}$; one parsec is equivalent to about 3×10^{16} m or $10^{16.5}$ m; the speed of light is about 3×10^8 m s^{-1} or $10^{8.5}$ m s^{-1}; and the relationship between photon energy and temperature (Equation 3.1) can be expressed as $E_{ph,mean} = 3 \times 10^{-4}T$ or $E_{ph,mean} = 10^{-3.5}T$ (where $E_{ph,mean}$ is in electronvolts and T is in kelvin). When multiplying together 'half powers of ten' such as this, the powers simply add as normal and give a whole number power, which is equivalent to saying that 3×3 is of the order of 10. This is illustrated by the following question.

● How far could a beam of light travel in one year?

○ Since distance = speed × time, the distance a beam of light could travel in one year is the speed of light multiplied by the number of seconds in one year. Namely:

distance = $(3 \times 10^8 \text{ m s}^{-1}) \times (3 \times 10^7 \text{ s})$

$= (10^{8.5} \text{ m s}^{-1}) \times (10^{7.5} \text{ s}) = 10^{(8.5 + 7.5)} \text{ m} = 10^{16} \text{ m}$

This distance is therefore one *light-year* and is equal to about one-third of a parsec.

11.2 The very early Universe

Time: $<10^{-36}$ s

Temperature: $>10^{28}$ K

Energy: $>3 \times 10^{15}$ GeV (i.e. $>3 \times 10^{24}$ eV)

At the very earliest times in the history of the Universe, we can only presume that a superunification of the four interactions was in operation. Unfortunately, no theory of superunification is yet available, so *nothing* can be said about the contents or behaviour of the Universe in its earliest moments. Indeed, it may even be that the concept of 'time' itself had no meaning until the Universe had cooled below a certain threshold.

The first stop on the tour where anything can be said is at about 5×10^{-44} s after the Big Bang — an epoch known as the Planck time. By this time the mean energy per particle in the Universe had fallen to around 10^{19} GeV (the Planck energy that you met in Section 10). This is the energy at which the gravitational force on an individual particle has roughly the same strength as its other interactions. An idea of the typical size scale of the Universe can be gained by thinking about how far a photon of light could have travelled during this period. By the time the Universe was 5×10^{-44} s old, a beam of light travelling at 3×10^8 m s^{-1} could have travelled a distance of only about 10^{-35} m. This tiny dimension is referred to as the Planck length.

⬤   How does the Planck length compare to the typical size of an atomic nucleus?

○   In Block 7, the typical size for an atomic nucleus was stated as about 10^{-14} m. So the Planck length is around 21 orders of magnitude smaller than an atomic nucleus. (It is as many times smaller than a nucleus as a nucleus is smaller than the Earth!)

As Figure 11.1 shows, at or around the Planck time, it is supposed that gravitational interactions became distinct from a grand unified interaction that included the three effects seen today as the electromagnetic, strong and weak interactions. In order to describe the gravitational interactions at these times a theory of quantum gravity is required. However, as you saw in Section 8, no such theory is yet available.

The temperature, and hence the mean energy per particle, was far higher at this time than can be recreated in particle accelerators here on Earth. Cosmologists and particle physicists can therefore only speculate on what might have occurred in the very early Universe. The best guess is that pairs of matter and antimatter particles of all types were spontaneously created out of pure energy, which can be thought of as a 'sea' of photons filling the entire Universe. With equal spontaneity, pairs of matter and antimatter particles also combined with each other again to produce photons. The overall process of pair creation (left to right) and annihilation (right to left) can be represented as:

$$\text{photons} \rightleftharpoons \text{particle} + \text{antiparticle} \tag{11.1}$$

At the temperatures existing in the Universe today, reactions such as this proceed preferentially from right to left. However, at the temperatures applying in the early Universe, the reactions proceeded in both directions at the same rate, for all types of particle. (This is analogous to the idea of chemical equilibria that you met in Block 8.) A stable situation was reached in which the rates of pair creation and annihilation exactly balanced, and equal amounts of matter/antimatter and radiation were maintained. In general, when a matter–antimatter pair undergoes annihilation, *two* photons are produced.

As well as the familiar quarks and leptons, if the Grand Unified Theory discussed in Section 10 is correct, then this is when the particles known as X bosons would also have been in evidence. These particles are the quanta of the grand unified interaction and are suggested as a means of *converting* between quarks and leptons, or between matter and antimatter. As the matter and antimatter X bosons decayed, they produced more quarks, antiquarks, leptons and antileptons — so adding to the raw materials from which the material contents of the Universe were later built. Using X to represent a matter X boson and $\overline{\text{X}}$ to represent an antimatter X boson, the type of reactions that are believed to have occurred are:

$$\text{X} \rightleftharpoons \text{quark} + \text{quark} \tag{11.2a}$$

$$\text{X} \rightleftharpoons \text{antiquark} + \text{antilepton} \tag{11.2b}$$

$$\overline{X} \rightleftharpoons \text{quark} + \text{lepton} \tag{11.2c}$$

$$\overline{X} \rightleftharpoons \text{antiquark} + \text{antiquark} \tag{11.2d}$$

As noted above, all six flavours of quark (u, d, c, s, t, b) and all six flavours of lepton (e^-, μ^-, τ^-, ν_e, ν_μ, ν_τ) that you met in Block 7 were produced at this time, along with their antiparticles. Notice, however, that matter and antimatter X bosons can each decay into *either* matter *or* antimatter particles. This will be important later on in the story.

The next stop in time is at about 10^{-36} s after the Big Bang when the Universe had a temperature of about 10^{28} K. This temperature marks the energy at which the strong interactions became distinct from the electroweak interactions (see Figure 11.1).

How long after the Planck time did the strong and electroweak interactions become distinct?

Be careful here!

$$10^{-36}\,\text{s} - 5 \times 10^{-44}\,\text{s} = (1 \times 10^{-36}\,\text{s}) - (0.000\,000\,05 \times 10^{-36}\,\text{s})$$
$$= 0.999\,999\,95 \times 10^{-36}\,\text{s}$$

So, to all intents and purposes, the strong and electroweak interactions became distinct about 10^{-36} s after the Planck time.

Question 11.2 (a) Suppose that some particular X bosons decay in the following manner:

$$X \longrightarrow u + d$$

$$X \longrightarrow \overline{u} + e^+$$

$$X \longrightarrow \overline{d} + \overline{\nu}_e$$

What must be the electric charge of these X bosons to ensure that electric charge is conserved?

(b) Write down the three equivalent reactions for the decay of an antimatter X boson. ◀

It should be emphasized that there is some disagreement and uncertainty about the exact processes that occurred at this extremely early period in the history of the Universe, but the story outlined above is the best guess at what may have actually occurred. Before proceeding with the trip through time, we will pause for a moment to examine a quite remarkable event that seems to have happened just after the strong and electroweak interactions became distinct. The event has profound consequences for the nature of the Universe today.

Activity 11.2 The contents of the Universe

This ongoing activity is revisited throughout Section 11, at the end of each subsection. It will help you to keep track of the 'contents' of the Universe as you progress through the various stages in its history. ◀

11.3 Inflation — a cosmic hiccup

Time: 10^{-36} s to 10^{-32} s

Temperature: rapidly changing

Energy: rapidly changing

In this section, two models for the expansion of the Universe soon after the Big Bang will be presented. The first model (known as the normal, or non-inflationary model) conflicts with current observations and has been superceded by the inflationary model. However, the non-inflationary model will be discussed first to introduce some basic ideas and to show why the inflationary model is necessary.

11.3.1 The non-inflationary model

When talking about the Universe, there is an important distinction that our discussion has, up until now, largely ignored. First, there is the entire Universe and this is probably infinite in size as mentioned in Section 2. By implication, it makes no sense to put a value on the 'size' of the entire Universe, since infinity is larger than any number you care to think of. But there is also what we may call the *observable* Universe, which is the region of space that it is theoretically *possible* for us to observe from Earth. We *can* calculate a value for the size of this finite region.

⬤ Why should there be a limit to how far we can see?

◯ The speed of light is a cosmic speed limit — nothing can travel any faster. So, the only part of the Universe that is now observable is that region of space from which light has had time to reach us since the Universe began, about 11 billion years ago.

In the non-inflationary model, the radius of the currently observable Universe is therefore equal to the maximum distance that light can have travelled since the Universe began. This is known as the **horizon distance** of the Universe, and is illustrated in Figure 11.3. (Note, however, that the horizon distance in the *inflationary* model is *not* equal to the radius of the currently observable Universe, for reasons that will be discussed later.)

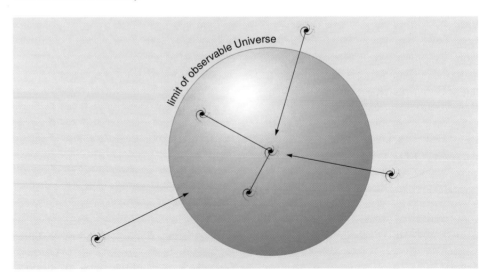

Figure 11.3 The size of the observable Universe. Imagine that the Earth lies at the centre of the circle (really a sphere in three dimensions), with a radius equal to the distance that light can travel since the Universe began. Then light from galaxies lying within the circle has had time to reach us, but light from galaxies lying outside the circle has not had sufficient time to reach us since the Universe began. Such galaxies are simply not observable at the current time. The circle therefore represents the horizon distance in a non-inflationary model for the expansion of the Universe.

Question 11.3   Assume for a moment that the Universe is *not* expanding. If the present age of the Universe is of the order of 10^{10} years, what is the current horizon distance? (Assume that the speed of light $c = 3 \times 10^8$ m s^{-1}, and that there are 3×10^7 s in one year.) ◄

Now, as you know from Section 2, the Universe *is* expanding and as a result the horizon distance in a non-inflationary model actually turns out to be three times *larger* than the estimate above would suggest. This is because the separation between objects was much smaller when the light started its travels, and space has expanded in the time it has taken light from distant objects to reach us. In symbols the horizon distance, $r_{horizon}$, at any time is given by

$$r_{horizon} = 3ct \qquad\qquad\qquad (11.3)$$

where t is the age of the Universe at the time in question and c is the speed of light. At the present time therefore, the horizon distance is about 3×10^{26} m. At earlier times, the horizon distance was correspondingly less, depending on the value of t at that time. The calculation to derive Equation 11.3 would be a lengthy detour from the story and we will not present it here. However, you can probably see that it is not unreasonable for the actual horizon distance to be larger in an expanding Universe than in one that is not expanding.

In practice the size of the currently observable Universe is very slightly less than the horizon distance calculated using Equation 11.3, since we can only see out to a distance that corresponds to the time when the photons last interacted with matter. Beyond this distance, the Universe is opaque to radiation, as if someone had drawn a curtain blocking our view of more remote epochs. The cosmic microwave background radiation that was discussed in Section 3 is a relic of this last interaction between matter and radiation. As you will see later, the time at which this happened was only about 300 000 years after the Big Bang. Since we don't even know the age of the Universe to an accuracy of a few billion years, this small difference in time is irrelevant. It makes no difference whether we use $t = 11 \times 10^9$ years or $t = (11 \times 10^9 - 3 \times 10^5)$ years in Equation 11.3. To all intents and purposes therefore, the horizon distance in the non-inflationary model represents the size of the currently observable Universe, as we stated earlier.

Now, since the Universe is expanding, the *size* of the region of space that is currently observable to us must have been smaller in the past. In order to quantify just how much smaller it was, we can look at how the temperature of the Universe has varied with time. At the epoch when the strong and electroweak interactions became distinct (10^{-36} s after the Big Bang), the temperature of the Universe was about 10^{28} K, whereas today, about eleven billion years later, the temperature is about 3 K.

○ By what factor was the Universe hotter than it is today, at the epoch when the strong and electroweak interactions became distinct?

○ The Universe was $\dfrac{10^{28}\ \mathrm{K}}{3\ \mathrm{K}} = 3 \times 10^{27}$ times hotter.

As described in Section 11.1, when the temperature of the Universe falls by a certain factor, the size of the Universe increases by the same factor. At the earlier epoch therefore, since the temperature was about 3×10^{27} times higher than now, the region of space that was destined to become the currently observable Universe, should have been 3×10^{27} times smaller than it is now.

Question 11.4 Assume that the currently observable Universe has a radius of about 3×10^{26} m, calculated from Equation 11.3, and that distances in the Universe have increased in size at the same rate as that at which the temperature has decreased. At the time when the strong and electroweak interactions became distinct, what was the radius of the region of space that was destined to expand to become the currently observable Universe? ◄

So, assuming that the temperature falls at the same rate as the Universe expands, then at the time when grand unification of the strong and electroweak interactions was just breaking down, the region of space that was destined to expand to become the currently observable Universe would have had a radius of only 10^{-1} m. This may seem like an incredibly small volume of space, but the problem is that it is actually far too large for comfort! To understand why, consider the following:

- What was the horizon distance at the time when the strong and electroweak interactions became distinct?

- Since this happened about 10^{-36} s after the Big Bang, the horizon distance at this time was

$$r_{horizon} = 3ct = 3 \times (3 \times 10^8 \text{ m s}^{-1}) \times (10^{-36} \text{ s})$$

$$= 10^{-27} \text{ m to the nearest order of magnitude}$$

So, at the time when the strong and electroweak interactions became distinct, the horizon distance was only 10^{-27} m. Yet, in this non-inflationary model for the expansion of the Universe, the region of space that was destined to expand to become the currently observable Universe would already have had a radius of 10^{-1} m. This situation is illustrated in Figure 11.4.

Figure 11.4 The horizon distance and the region of space that was destined to expand to become the currently observable Universe (a) at 10^{-36} s after the Big Bang and (b) today, assuming a non-inflationary model for the expansion of the Universe. The horizon distance increases steadily with time as described by Equation 11.3. The size of the observable Universe grows at a much slower rate, only increasing by a factor of ten for every hundredfold increase in time, as explained in Section 11.1.

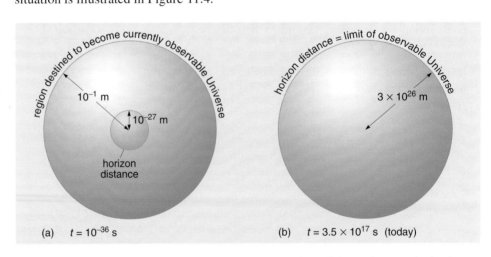

In fact, in this non-inflationary model for the expansion of the Universe, the horizon distance was much *smaller* than the radius of the currently observable Universe at *all* times in the past. And herein lies a problem. Namely how to explain the overall structure of the Universe that is observed today. The results from the COBE satellite (Section 3) showed that one part of the Universe has exactly the same temperature, to an accuracy of better than one part in ten thousand, as any other part of the Universe (see the picture on the title page). Furthermore, the expansion rate of the Universe in one direction is observed to be exactly the same as that in any other direction. In other words, the observable Universe today is seen to be incredibly uniform or *smooth*. At 10^{-36} s after the Big Bang, when things were closer together than they are now by a factor of 3×10^{27}, the physical conditions across the Universe must therefore have been identical to an unimaginable level of accuracy.

When the Universe began, there is absolutely no reason why it should have been so incredibly uniform. It is far more likely that the uniformity arose slightly later as energy redistributed itself. However, any 'smoothing' process that redistributes energy around the early Universe cannot propagate faster than the speed of light — it's the cosmic speed limit again. But the region of space that was destined to become the currently observable Universe was, at this very early time, enormously larger than the distance over which light could possibly have travelled (Figure 11.4). How could the Universe have arrived in such a smooth, uniform state, today when any smoothing process would have operated over such a tiny distance? Considering the situation we see today, illustrated in Figure 11.5, how is it that two regions of space which we see in opposite directions, are expanding and cooling at exactly the same rate, if they have *never* been in contact with each other?

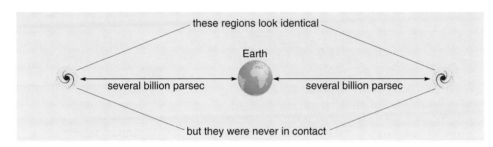

these regions look identical

Earth

several billion parsec   several billion parsec

but they were never in contact

Figure 11.5 Two regions of space seen in opposite directions, each several billion parsecs away, look identical. Yet, according to the non-inflationary model for the expansion of the Universe, they have never been in contact with each other. Each is outside the other's horizon distance.

11.3.2 The inflationary model

The picture presented so far cannot explain the uniformity of the Universe — if that's the only model on offer then the uniformity must simply be assumed as an initial condition that is somehow put in at the start of things.

A far more satisfactory solution to this problem (and a couple of others that cannot be gone into here) is known as **inflation**. In 1981, the American physicist Alan Guth suggested that, in the early history of the Universe at times between about 10^{-36} s and 10^{-32} s after the Big Bang, the Universe underwent a period of hugely accelerated expansion. During this time, distances in the Universe expanded by an extraordinary factor — something like 10^{50} has been suggested although this could be a vast underestimate! Inflation is believed to be caused by the way in which the strong and electroweak interactions became distinct.

The exact mechanism by which inflation occurred is not important here, but there are many consequences of this theory. The most important consequence for the present discussion concerns the currently observable Universe. Remember, this is a spherical volume with a radius of 3×10^{26} m, corresponding to the distance that light could travel since the time (300 000 years after the Big Bang) when radiation last interacted with matter. As shown in Figure 11.6a, the region of space that was destined to expand to become the currently observable Universe, originated in an extremely tiny region of the pre-inflated Universe — a region that was at least 10^{50} times smaller than the 10^{-1} m radius we calculated earlier. This tiny region was far smaller than the horizon distance at that time, 10^{-27} m, and so any smoothing processes could have operated throughout the space that now constitutes the observable Universe. The problem of the uniformity of the microwave background and the uniform measured expansion then goes away.

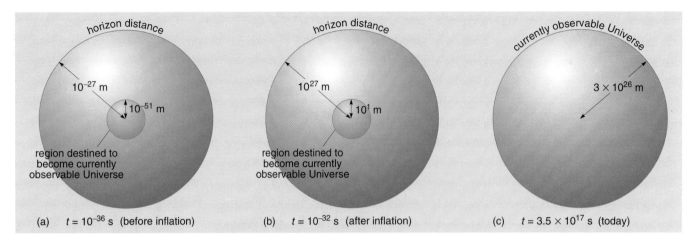

horizon distance

10^{-27} m

10^{-51} m

region destined to become currently observable Universe

(a) $t = 10^{-36}$ s (before inflation)

horizon distance

10^{27} m

10^1 m

region destined to become currently observable Universe

(b) $t = 10^{-32}$ s (after inflation)

currently observable Universe

3×10^{26} m

(c) $t = 3.5 \times 10^{17}$ s (today)

Figure 11.6 (a) The region of space that was destined to expand to become the currently observable Universe originated in an extremely tiny region of the pre-inflated Universe. This tiny region was far smaller than the horizon distance at that time, and so any smoothing processes could have operated throughout the space that now constitutes the observable Universe. (b) After inflation the region of space destined to become the currently observable Universe and the horizon distance were each at least 10^{50} times larger than they would have been were there no inflation. (c) By the present day, the observable Universe has expanded to a radius of around 3×10^{26} m, and the inflationary horizon distance is even larger.

After inflation had finished (Figure 11.6b), when the Universe was around 10^{-32} s old, both the horizon distance and the radius of the region of space that was destined to become the currently observable Universe were at least 10^{50} times larger than they would have been were there no inflation. Today, 11 billion years later (Figure 11.6c), the currently observable Universe has a radius of 3×10^{26} m. This is the same as the size of the currently observable Universe calculated earlier, using Equation 11.3, for the non-inflationary model. However, the horizon distance in this inflationary model (which we can call the *inflationary horizon distance*) is much larger than in the non-inflationary model, thanks to the vast increase in scale that was accumulated during inflation.

In the inflationary model, therefore, the horizon distance is *always* much larger than the radius of the region of space that is destined to become the currently observable Universe. Non-uniformities may still be out there, but they are far beyond the limits of the observable Universe — and always will be. Because we cannot ever hope to see beyond this barrier, we can have no knowledge whatsoever of events that occurred *before* inflation, since any information about such events is washed out by the rapid increase in scale. Inflation serves to hide from us any event, process or structure that was present in the Universe at the very earliest times.

Question 11.5 (a) How do the horizon distance and the radius of the region of space that was destined to become the currently observable Universe compare with each other in the inflationary model and in the non-inflationary model at early times?

(b) How do the two distances compare in the two models at the present time? ◄

If you're thinking that the inflation theory contains some pretty bizarre ideas — you're right! — but it's the most promising theory that currently exists for one of the earliest phases in the history of the Universe. We shall say no more about it here, but now pick up the story again after the Universe has completed its cosmic hiccup. The strong and electroweak interactions have now become distinct, and the X bosons have largely disappeared as described by Equation 11.2.

Activity 11.2   The contents of the Universe (continued)

Revisit this activity and add the contents of the Universe after inflation to your summary. ◄

11.4 The quark–lepton era

Time: 10^{-11} s to 10^{-5} s

Temperature: 3×10^{15} K to 3×10^{12} K

Energy: 1 000 GeV to 1 GeV

During the time interval 10^{-32} s to 10^{-11} s, i.e. for the 10^{-11} seconds or so after inflation, nothing new happened in the Universe! It merely carried on expanding and cooling, but no new processes took place. The desert (as it is known) came to an end when the Universe reached a temperature of about 3×10^{15} K, and this is where the next stage in our history begins. At this point the mean energy per particle was around 1 000 GeV and the electromagnetic and weak interactions became distinct (Figure 11.1). As you saw in Section 10, the energies corresponding to this transition are becoming attainable in experiments here on Earth. So it could be argued that all particle reactions that models propose after the first 10^{-11} s of the history of the Universe are *directly* testable in Earth-based laboratories.

By 10^{-11} s after the Big Bang, the X bosons had long since decayed in reactions like those shown in Equation 11.2, but the temperature of the Universe was still too high for the familiar baryons (protons and neutrons) to be stable. The Universe contained all types of leptons, quarks, antileptons, and antiquarks as well as photons. In fact, there would have been approximately equal numbers of particles and antiparticles at this time — but note that word *approximately* — we shall return to the implications of this in a moment. There would also have been equal amounts of radiation (photons) and matter/antimatter (particles or antiparticles).

Question 11.6   Now is a good time to revise your knowledge of the fundamental particles from which the Universe is built. These particles are listed on the Study Guide for this block.

(a) How do the properties of one generation of particles differ from those of each other generation?

(b) Which particles participate in strong interactions, weak interactions and electromagnetic interactions, respectively?

(c) How do the electric charge and mass of antimatter particles differ from the corresponding matter particles? ◀

Let's now consider what the net electric charge of the Universe would have been at this time. When quarks and leptons are spontaneously produced from energy (Equation 11.1), they appear as matter–antimatter pairs with equal and opposite charge. So the net charge of the Universe remains zero, however many quarks, antiquarks, leptons and antileptons are produced in this way. But there is another way of producing leptons and quarks, namely by the decay of X bosons (Equation 11.2). The decays of X bosons produce:

- three quarks for every one lepton (and three antiquarks for every antilepton);

- quarks with charge $+\frac{2}{3}e$ as often as quarks with charge $-\frac{1}{3}e$;

- charged leptons as often as uncharged leptons.

So, a few X bosons might decay to produce three up quarks, three down quarks, one electron and one electron neutrino, in accordance with these rules.

○ What is the total electric charge of: three up quarks, three down quarks, one electron and one electron neutrino?

○ The charge of a single up quark is $+\frac{2}{3}e$, of a single down quark is $-\frac{1}{3}e$, of a single electron is $-e$, and of a single electron neutrino is 0. So the total charge of this collection of particles is $(3 \times \frac{2}{3}e) - (3 \times \frac{1}{3}e) - e + 0 = 0$.

An X boson decay rate with a three to one balance between quarks and leptons therefore ensured that the net charge of the Universe remained zero.

The next stage of the story is to look at how and when the original mixture of all types of quarks and leptons, that were present when the Universe was 10^{-11} s old, gave rise to the Universe today which seems to be dominated by protons, neutrons and electrons.

○ In particle accelerators, how much energy is required in order to 'create' a particle and antiparticle of a given mass?

○ Broadly speaking, an amount of energy equal to (or greater than) the equivalent mass of the particle and antiparticle concerned needs to be supplied. (For example, the mass of an electron is $511 \, \text{keV}/c^2$, so to create an electron–positron pair, at least $2 \times 511 \, \text{keV}$ of energy must be available.)

In the early Universe, when the mean energy per particle was greater than the mass of a given particle plus antiparticle, they existed in abundance, and survived in equilibrium with radiation as described by Equation 11.1. When the mean energy per particle dropped below this value, annihilations became more likely than pair creations, and so the number of particles and antiparticles of a given type reduced.

Massive quarks and leptons also decay into less massive ones, and these decays became more likely as the available energy fell. You saw an example of this type of process in Figure 7.1b, where a muon decayed into an electron, a muon neutrino and an electron antineutrino.

○ In the early Universe, what was the mean energy per particle when the following particles decayed into their less massive counterparts? (a) Top quarks with mass around $180 \, \text{GeV}/c^2$. (b) Tauons with mass around $1.8 \, \text{GeV}/c^2$.

○ (a) Top quarks decayed when the mean energy per particle fell below about $180 \, \text{GeV}$. (b) Tauons decayed when the mean energy per particle fell below about $1.8 \, \text{GeV}$.

Broadly speaking, when the temperature of the Universe fell below that at which the mean energy per particle was similar to the mass equivalent of the particles concerned, then the particles decayed into other less massive particles. So, by the time the Universe had cooled to a temperature of 3×10^{12} K, equivalent to a mean energy per particle of about 1 GeV, when the Universe was 10^{-5} s old, several important changes had taken place. First, many of the tauons and antitauons, muons and antimuons had decayed into their less massive lepton counterparts: electrons and positrons. Also, the temperature had fallen such that the reaction in Equation 11.1 favoured annihilation rather than pair creation for tauons and muons, so any remaining massive leptons had mutually annihilated, producing photons. The only leptons that remained in the Universe in any significant number were therefore electrons and neutrinos (with their antiparticles in approximately equal numbers).

Similarly, the massive quarks (strange, charm, top and bottom) had mostly decayed into their less massive counterparts (up and down), via a variety of transformations, some of which are shown in Figure 11.7. Notice that all of these decays are weak interactions, since they involve W bosons. In each case quarks change flavour with the emission of a lepton–antilepton pair.

Question 11.7   Figure 11.7 shows how top and bottom quarks can decay into bottom and charm quarks, respectively. Following the patterns shown here, draw Feynman diagrams to represent: (a) the decay of a charm quark into a strange quark, and (b) the decay of a strange quark into an up quark.◀

All types of quarks and antiquarks also underwent mutual annihilations — with a particularly crucial result. In discussing the relative numbers of particles and antiparticles earlier, the phrase *approximately* equal was used deliberately. If the Universe had contained *exactly* equal numbers of quarks and antiquarks, then these would have all annihilated each other, leaving a Universe that contained no baryons — so no protons and neutrons — no atoms and molecules — no galaxies, stars, planets or people. Clearly that is *not* what we observe around us!

In fact the Universe now seems to consist almost entirely of matter (rather than antimatter) in the form of protons, neutrons, electrons and electron neutrinos, plus photons. And there are believed to be roughly one billion photons for every baryon (proton or neutron) in the Universe today. This implies that, just before the quark–antiquark annihilations took place, for every billion antimatter quarks there must have been *just over* a billion matter quarks. Running the Universe forward from this point, for every billion quarks and billion antiquarks that annihilated each other producing photons, a few quarks were left over to build baryons in order to make galaxies, stars, planets and people.

Why did the Universe produce this slight imbalance of matter over antimatter? Maybe it was just 'built-in' from the start, like any other constant of nature? This is rather unsatisfactory to many cosmologists and particle physicists who prefer to believe that the imbalance arose *after* the Universe had got started. It has been suggested that the decays of X bosons into quarks and leptons *may* slightly favour the production of matter particles over antimatter particles. As you saw in Equation 11.2, a matter or antimatter X boson can decay into *either* matter particles or antimatter particles. So, if there is an imbalance in the rates, starting with equal numbers of matter and antimatter X bosons *will not* lead to the production of equal numbers of matter and antimatter quarks and leptons. Such matter–antimatter asymmetry has actually already been observed with experiments on Earth that measure the decay of particles called K mesons. Of the two possible routes for this reaction, one is favoured over the other by seven parts in a thousand. Perhaps something similar, to the tune of a few parts in a billion, occurs with X boson decays? The answer to this question is not yet known — but it's a rather important one, since without it none of us would be here to discuss the matter!

Activity 11.2   The contents of the Universe (continued)

Revisit this activity and add the contents of the Universe at this time to your summary.◀

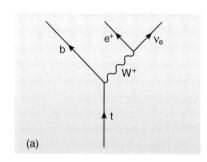

(a)

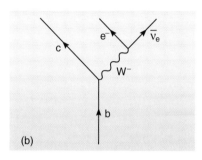

(b)

Figure 11.7   Feynman diagrams showing some examples of processes by which massive quarks decay into less massive quarks. In each case, electric charge, the number of quarks minus the number of antiquarks, and the number of leptons minus the number of antileptons are all conserved.

11.5 The hadron era

Time: 10^{-5} s to 100 s

Temperature: 3×10^{12} K to 10^9 K

Energy: 1 GeV to 300 keV

From the time that the temperature fell to about 3×10^{12} K, at about 10^{-5} s after the Big Bang, stable baryons (protons and neutrons) began to form from the up and down quarks that remained after the annihilation of matter and antimatter.

○ How does the mean energy per particle at 10^{-5} s compare with the equivalent mass of a proton or neutron?

○ Protons and neutrons have a mass of about 1 GeV/c^2, which is similar to the mean energy per particle in the Universe at this time.

This is why confinement of quarks became important from this time onwards. Before 10^{-5} s after the Big Bang, there had been sufficient energy available for up and down quarks to escape to distances significantly larger than the dimensions of a proton or neutron. After this time, no such escape was possible.

○ What are the quark contents of a proton and a neutron?

○ Recall from earlier in the block that a proton is composed of two up quarks and a down quark, whereas a neutron is composed of two down quarks and an up quark.

Equal numbers of up and down quarks therefore led to an equal number of protons and neutrons emerging from this process. To recap on the contents of the Universe at this time, there were about a billion photons, electrons, positrons, neutrinos and antineutrinos for every single proton or neutron in the Universe.

○ Why had the electrons and positrons not yet mutually annihilated each other?

○ The mass of an electron or positron is 511 keV/c^2, and the mean energy per particle was still much higher than the 1 MeV required to create a pair of them. So electrons and positrons were still in equilibrium with photons, undergoing both annihilation and pair creation reactions at the same rate.

As soon as baryons had formed, weak interactions took over, with protons and neutrons existing in an equilibrium governed by the following processes:

$$e^+ + n \rightleftharpoons p + \bar{\nu}_e \tag{11.4a}$$

$$\nu_e + n \rightleftharpoons p + e^- \tag{11.4b}$$

So neutrons converted into protons by reacting with either positrons or electron neutrinos; whilst protons converted into neutrons by reacting with either electron antineutrinos or electrons.

○ At the quark and lepton level, how can the two reactions in Equation 11.4 be represented?

Bearing in mind the quark composition of a proton and a neutron, each of the reactions involve conversions between a down quark and an up quark as shown in Equations 11.5a and b:

$$e^+ + d \rightleftharpoons u + \bar{v}_e \qquad \text{(11.5a)}$$

$$v_e + d \rightleftharpoons u + e^- \qquad \text{(11.5b)}$$

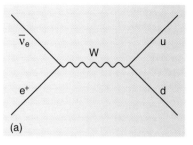

(a)

We can also draw Feynman diagrams to illustrate these two processes, as shown in Figure 11.8. Each of the two processes may be considered as arising from the *exchange* of a W boson.

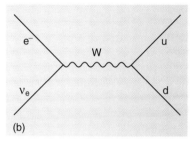

(b)

With plenty of energy available, the transitions from neutron to proton and from proton to neutron proceeded at the same rate. Since there were as many neutrinos as electrons, and as many antineutrinos as positrons, the numbers of neutrons and protons in the Universe remained equal, at least initially. However, this situation did not continue. As noted in Section 7.3, the mass of a neutron is slightly higher than that of a proton. As a consequence of this, the reactions in which a proton converted into a neutron became slightly less likely to happen as the energy fell, because they required more energy than those in which a neutron was converted into a proton. As the Universe cooled, this difference in the rates of the two processes became more pronounced, and protons began to outnumber neutrons for the first time.

As the Universe cooled still further another reaction became important for the neutrons and the protons: as you saw in Section 7.3 isolated neutrons decay into protons. This additional process, again governed by the weak interaction, added to the dominance of protons over neutrons in the Universe:

$$n \longrightarrow p + e^- + \bar{v}_e \qquad \text{(11.6)}$$

Figure 11.8 (a) and (b) Feynman diagrams illustrating the reactions occurring in Equations 11.5a and b, respectively. No arrows are shown because each of these Feynman diagrams can be read either from bottom to top (neutron to proton conversions), or from top to bottom (proton to neutron conversions). The W boson in each case may be exchanged either from left to right or from right to left. Positrons, electron neutrinos, and up quarks will emit W^+ bosons, whereas electrons, electron antineutrinos and down quarks will emit W^- bosons.

Question 11.8 At the quark and lepton level, how may Reaction 11.6 be represented? Draw a Feynman diagram to represent the weak process occurring and show how it is mediated by a W^- boson. ◀

Once the Universe was 0.1 s old, the weak interactions described by the reactions in Equations 11.4 and 11.5 became too slow, and neutrinos virtually ceased to have any further interaction with the rest of the Universe — ever! The ratio of protons to neutrons continued to rise as a result of Equation 11.6, and was only halted (see Section 11.6) when the neutrons became bound up in atomic nuclei where they became essentially immune from decay. As you saw in Section 7.3, if the half-life of the neutron (about 10 minutes) were much shorter than it in fact is, then all neutrons would have decayed into protons long before they could become confined inside nuclei.

When the Universe was about 10 s old, when the mean energy per particle was about 1 MeV, a final important event for the matter contents of the Universe occurred when the remaining primordial electrons and positrons mutually annihilated, producing yet more photons, but leaving the excess one-in-a-billion electrons to balance the charges of the primordial one-in-a-billion protons and ensure that the Universe has a net electric charge of zero.

Activity 11.2   The contents of the Universe (continued)

Revisit this activity and add the contents of the Universe at this time to your summary. ◀

11.6 Primordial nucleosynthesis

Time: 100 s to 1 000 s

Temperature: 10^9 K to 3×10^8 K

Energy: 300 keV to 100 keV

As the temperature continued to decrease, protons and neutrons were able to combine to make light nuclei. This marked the beginning of the period referred to as the era of primordial **nucleosynthesis** (which literally means 'making nuclei'). The first such reaction to become energetically favoured was that of a single proton and neutron combining to produce a deuterium nucleus, with the excess energy carried away by a γ-ray photon:

$$n + p \rightleftharpoons \, {}^{2}_{1}H + \gamma \tag{11.7}$$

○ What is deuterium?

○ Recall from Section 9 that deuterium is an *isotope* of hydrogen. Whereas normal hydrogen nuclei consist simply of a proton, deuterium nuclei (sometimes called 'heavy hydrogen') contain a proton and a neutron.

At high temperatures (greater than 10^9 K), there are a lot of high-energy photons so this reaction is favoured to go from right to left. (Recall how chemical equilibria are pushed one way or the other when one of the reactants dominates.) As a result, deuterium nuclei were rapidly broken down. However, as the temperature fell below 10^9 K when the Universe was about 100 s old, deuterium production was favoured. Virtually all of the remaining free neutrons in the Universe were rapidly bound up in deuterium nuclei, and from then on other light nuclei formed. One of the reactions that occurred was:

$$ {}^{2}_{1}H + {}^{2}_{1}H \rightarrow {}^{3}_{1}H + p \tag{11.8a}$$

$$ {}^{3}_{1}H + {}^{2}_{1}H \rightarrow {}^{4}_{2}He + n \tag{11.8b}$$

○ What is the nucleus represented by ${}^{3}_{1}H$ in Equation 11.8?

○ This represents a nucleus of another isotope of hydrogen (called tritium) which contains two neutrons and one proton.

Equation 11.8a shows that two deuterium nuclei react together to form a nucleus of tritium with the ejection of a proton. The tritium nucleus immediately reacts with another deuterium nucleus (Equation 11.8b) to form a nucleus of helium-4 with the emission of a neutron. The proton and neutron produced in the two reactions above can combine to form another deuterium nucleus (Equation 11.7), so the *net* result of this set of reactions is that two deuterium nuclei are converted into a single nucleus of helium-4.

Other more massive nuclei were also made as follows:

(11.9a)

(11.9b)

or

(11.9c)

(11.9d)

Equation 11.9a shows that deuterium nuclei react with protons to make nuclei of helium-3. These can then either react with other helium-3 nuclei to make helium-4 plus more protons (Equation 11.9b) or with nuclei of helium-4 to make beryllium-7 (Equation 11.9c). Nuclei of beryllium-7 are unstable and immediately capture an electron to form lithium-7 with the emission of an electron antineutrino. Lithium-7 nuclei can react further (Equation 11.9d) with a proton to create nuclei of beryllium-8, but these too are unstable and immediately split apart into a pair of helium-4 nuclei. The end products of the four reactions (Equations 11a to d) are nuclei of helium-3, helium-4 and lithium-7, with the vast majority ending up as helium-4.

Question 11.9   The reactions in Equation 11.9 are the same as those that comprise the later stages of the proton–proton chain that occurs in the Sun (Section 9). Why did the first stage of the proton–proton chain not occur to any great extent in the early Universe? (*Hint*: Refer back to Section 9 to look at the *time-scale* for this reaction.) ◀

Nuclei with a mass number greater than seven did not survive in the early Universe. This is because there are no stable nuclei with a mass number of eight — notice from Equation 11.9 that the beryllium nuclei decay spontaneously, leading ultimately to more helium-4. The reactions that by-pass this bottleneck take much longer than the few minutes that were available for nucleosynthesis at this time. (Remember, we're now talking about a time-span of around 15 minutes when the Universe had an age of between 100 and 1 000 s.) Before more advanced reactions could occur, the Universe cooled too much to provide the energy necessary to initiate them.

Question 11.10   In addition to the 'barrier' at a mass number of eight, there are also no stable nuclei with a mass number of five. Using the building blocks available in the early Universe, what nuclei could you combine to try to create a nucleus with a mass number of five? Why do you think the resulting nuclei would be unstable? ◀

The ratio of protons to neutrons had, by this time, reached about seven protons for every one neutron. Because the neutrons were bound up in nuclei, they no longer decayed, and the ratio remained essentially fixed from here on. The vast majority of the neutrons ended up in nuclei of helium-4. Only very tiny fractions were left in deuterium, helium-3 and lithium-7 nuclei, since the reactions to produce them were far more likely to continue and produce helium-4 than they were to halt at these intermediate products.

By the time the Universe had cooled to a temperature of about 3×10^8 K after 1 000 s, the particles had insufficient energy to undergo any more reactions. The era of primordial nucleosynthesis was at an end, and the proportion of the various light elements was fixed. The rates of reaction to form helium and the other light elements have been calculated and the abundances predicted may be compared with the abundances of these nuclei that are observed in the Universe today. There is close agreement between theory and observation.

> The close agreement between the theoretically predicted abundances of the light elements and the observed abundances in the Universe today is the third major piece of evidence, alongside the cosmic microwave background and the Hubble expansion, in favour of the hot big bang model for the origin of the Universe (see Section 3.3).

At an age of 1 000 s, the Universe reached a state where its matter constituents were essentially as they are today. There are about 10^9 photons for every baryon (proton and neutron), and about seven protons and electrons for every one neutron. Neutrinos and antineutrinos continue to travel through the Universe unhindered by virtually anything they encounter.

Question 11.11   Assume that the Universe contains 1 neutron for every 7 protons, and that all the neutrons are today bound up in nuclei of helium-4.

(a) What are the relative numbers of hydrogen and helium nuclei in the Universe?

(b) What are the relative percentages, by mass, of hydrogen and helium in the Universe? (*Hint*: Assume that protons and neutrons each have a mass of 'one unit'.) ◀

Activity 11.2   The contents of the Universe (continued)

Revisit this activity and add the contents of the Universe at this time to your summary. ◀

11.7 Structure in the Universe

Time: 10^{10} s to 3.5×10^{17} s (300 years to 11 billion years)

Temperature: 10^5 K to 2.73 K

Energy: 30 eV to 6.3×10^{-4} eV

As the Universe cooled still further, nothing much happened for a few hundred years (between 1 000 s and 10^{10} s). As the mean energy per particle fell below the ionization energies of hydrogen and helium atoms (13.6 eV and 24.6 eV, respectively, see Block 7), so electrons began to combine with nuclei to form neutral atoms.

Gradually, as this electrically neutral matter accumulated, gravity began to take over as the dominant force operating in the Universe. Slight variations in the amount of matter and radiation in different regions meant that matter began to gather together into slightly denser clumps. These clumps provided the seeds from which galaxies later grew.

By the time the Universe had cooled to a temperature of 3 000 K, about 300 000 years after the Big Bang, the mean energy of the photons had fallen to about 1 eV, and most of the matter in the Universe was in the form of neutral atoms. This was the trigger for another significant change in the behaviour of the Universe. The background radiation photons — those 10^9 photons for every particle left over from the quark–lepton era — interacted for the last time with matter in the Universe. From this point on, there were virtually no photons with energies large enough to excite electrons from the ground states of hydrogen and helium atoms, so photons were no longer absorbed by matter. After this time, the cosmic background radiation simply expanded freely with the Universe, cooling as it did so. When the cosmic microwave background radiation is observed today, very slight irregularities are observed in its temperature and intensity. These reflect slight differences in the matter distribution of the Universe at the time of the last interaction between the background photons and atoms. At the time of the discovery of these irregularities by the COBE satellite (Section 3.2), they were described as 'wrinkles in the fabric of space–time' (see the picture on the title page).

Some time after the last interaction of matter and radiation, but probably before the Universe was a billion years old, the first galaxies formed. The exact time for this event is uncertain, but within these early galaxies, stars condensed out of the gas to become dense enough for nuclear reactions to start within their cores. Deep within these stars, hydrogen was converted into helium, releasing energy as electromagnetic radiation into the Universe. As stars age, so their cores contract and grow hotter, allowing helium fusion to occur. These further reactions produce heavier nuclei such as carbon, oxygen and silicon. The more massive the star, the hotter its interior, and the more massive the elements that can be produced by nuclear fusion reactions. But there is a limit to how far nuclear fusion can go. As you saw in Section 9, when four protons are converted into a nucleus of helium-4, the products have a lower mass than the reactants. This mass difference is liberated as energy. Similar mass reductions apply for reactions to produce all the elements up to those with mass numbers in the range of about 56 to 62, such as iron, cobalt and nickel. However, for nuclear fusion reactions beyond this, more energy must be put into the reactions than is released from them, so these are not viable.

Figure 11.9 The Crab nebula, a supernova remnant in the constellation of Taurus. This expanding cloud of gas was thrown off in a recent supernova explosion when a massive star reached the end of its life. The cloud seen here is about three parsecs across. The exploding star was seen by Chinese astronomers on 4 July 1054, and was so bright that it remained visible in full daylight for 23 days.

As the most massive stars approach the ends of their lives, when their cores are composed of nuclei that undergo no more fusion, some nuclear reactions within their interiors release free neutrons. These neutrons can then add, slowly one at a time, to the iron, cobalt or nickel nuclei to make even more massive elements. As more and more neutrons are added, some transform into protons, via β^--decay, and in this way massive (stable) nuclei up to $^{209}_{83}\mathrm{Bi}$ (bismuth) can be created. This is the most massive, non-radioactive nucleus that exists in the Universe.

But what happens to these massive stars? When the core is largely composed of iron, they have no further source of energy available. The outer layers fall inwards, squeezing the centre of the star down until it has a density comparable to that of an atomic nucleus. The collapse halts — suddenly — and the material rebounds, setting off a shock wave back through the outer layers of the star. The result is a so-called *supernova explosion*, in which 90% of the star's mass is thrown violently out into space (see Figure 11.9). In the final moments of its life, the star has one final surprise left. The immense temperatures and pressures created during the explosion cause electrons and protons to react to form huge numbers of free neutrons (Equation 11.4b, right to left). These neutrons enable elements to be built *beyond* the bismuth limit. All naturally radioactive elements in the Universe (apart from those which are the decay products of even more massive radioactive nuclei) were formed in such supernovae explosions, and a large proportion of the others between nickel and bismuth were also created in these violent events.

From here the star cycle repeats — but this time with a slight difference. Stars that formed after the first generation had lived and died had a richer source of raw material. A star like the Sun was formed in a galaxy that had already seen at least one generation of massive stars born, live and die in supernovae explosions. The gas and dust from which the Sun formed had therefore been enriched by heavier elements produced inside these earlier stars. This leads to the possibility of the formation of planets from the rubble left behind.

The Earth itself formed from such debris. Every nucleus of carbon, oxygen, nitrogen and silicon found on the Earth and within living creatures was created inside the heart of an ancient star. Every nucleus of precious metal such as silver, gold and platinum was formed either from slow neutron capture in ageing stars, or by rapid neutron capture during the supernova explosions that mark their death. And so we come full circle back to the present day. About 3.5×10^{17} s after the Big Bang, when the Universe has cooled to only 2.73 K.

Homing in on a fairly average spiral galaxy, we find a fairly average star somewhere out in one its spiral arms. Orbiting this star is a small rocky planet, two-thirds covered with water, and with an atmosphere rich in oxygen. On the surface of the planet are many living creatures, including members of one species who are so interested in the origin and complexity of the Universe that they build telescopes and particle accelerators with which to study it. They observe the expansion of the Universe by the red-shift of distant galaxies, and the cooling of the Universe by the spectrum of its background radiation. Using particle accelerators they recreate extreme temperatures and examine particle reactions that have not occurred in the Universe for billions of years. The revelations of such experiments confirm that no epoch or location in the Universe is subject to any special dispensation. That at all times and all places the same physical principles hold, yet manifest themselves in a gloriously evolving diversity.

Activity 11.2 The contents of the Universe (continued)

Revisit this activity for the last time and complete your summary by adding the contents of the Universe today. ◀

Question 11.12 A small region of the early Universe contains two billion and twelve matter X bosons, two billion and twelve antimatter X bosons, and four billion photons. A billion of the matter X bosons each decay into an antimatter quark and an antimatter lepton (Equation 11.2b); and a billion of the antimatter X bosons each decay into a pair of antiquarks (Equation 11.2d). The remaining billion and twelve matter X bosons each decay into a pair of quarks (Equation 11.2a) and the remaining billion and twelve antimatter X bosons each decay into a quark and a lepton (Equation 11.2c).

Remember, you can use 'A history of the Universe' on the Block 11 CD-ROM to help you answer the following questions.

(a) After the matter and antimatter X bosons have decayed, how many quarks, antiquarks, lepton, antileptons and photons are there in this region of the Universe? (*Hint*: Use Equation 11.2.)

(b) After the matter and antimatter quarks and leptons have annihilated each other, how many matter quarks and leptons are left over? How many photons are now present? (*Hint*: Use Equation 11.1.)

(c) Assuming that half of the remaining quarks are up quarks and half are down quarks, how many protons and neutrons can be made?

(d) Assuming that half of the leptons are electrons and half are electron neutrinos, what is the final composition of this region of the Universe? ◀

Question 11.13 (a) Describe three times or sites at which nucleosynthesis has occurred in the history of the Universe.

(b) At which of these times or sites did most of the (i) helium, (ii) oxygen, and (iii) uranium in the Universe originate? ◀

Question 11.14 In which order did the following events occur in the history of the Universe? (*Hint*: Consider the energy required for each process.)

(i) the formation of atoms

(ii) the formation of light nuclei

(iii) the formation of quarks and leptons

(iv) the formation of protons and neutrons

(v) the annihilation of electrons and positrons

(vi) the annihilation of quarks and antiquarks

(vii) neutrinos cease to interact with matter or radiation

(viii) background photons cease to interact with matter ◀

Question 11.15 What are the three key pieces of observational evidence that support the idea of a hot big bang? Which of them do you think allows cosmologists to reach back furthest into the past, and why? ◀

11.8 Summary of Section 11

The Universe was created at the instant of the Big Bang. As it has aged, the Universe has cooled and distances within it have increased. At the earliest times, the four fundamental interactions were unified, but as the temperature of the Universe decreased, so these interactions became distinct.

The earliest time about which anything can be said is the Planck time, when the gravitational interaction had a similar strength to the other fundamental interactions. Before this, the concept of 'time' itself may have no meaning.

Early in its history, the Universe is presumed to have undergone a hugely accelerated period of expansion, known as inflation. One effect of this was to smooth out any irregularities, leading to an observable Universe today that is remarkably uniform.

The early Universe contained *almost* equal numbers of matter and antimatter particles (quarks and leptons). However, there was an asymmetry of a few parts per billion in favour of matter. The matter and antimatter underwent mutual annihilation and the result of this is that there are now about 10^9 photons for every matter particle in the Universe.

Equal numbers of protons and neutrons were initially produced in the Universe from the up and down quarks remaining after annihilation. However, free neutrons decay, and this reduced their number, leading to a Universe containing about seven protons for every neutron today.

All free neutrons were soon bound up within nuclei of deuterium, helium and lithium. The approximate distribution of mass in the Universe is about 25% helium-4 to 75% hydrogen, with small traces of other nuclei.

Neutrinos ceased to interact with the rest of the Universe soon after protons and neutrons were formed.

Photons produced from the matter–antimatter annihilations had their last interaction with the matter of the Universe 300 000 years after the Big Bang, when the temperature was about 3 000 K. These photons, red-shifted by a factor of a thousand by the expansion of the Universe, form the cosmic microwave background that is observed today.

As the Universe cooled still further, galaxies and stars were able to form under the influence of gravity. Stars process light nuclei into heavier ones within their cores. The more massive stars then undergo supernova explosions, throwing material out into space ready to be included in later generations of stars and planets.

Activity 11.1   A history of the Universe (revisited)

If you have not yet looked at the CD-ROM activity 'A history of the Universe', do so now and try some of the tasks in the Study File. ◄

The future of the Universe

12

So what is the future of the Universe? Will it go on expanding and cooling for ever? Or does it have another fate in store? The short answer is that no one knows, but at least two possibilities can be suggested.

These questions may be considered with the help of an analogy, namely that of launching an object from the surface of a planet, as shown in Figure 12.1. If a rocket is launched with a small amount of kinetic energy, it will eventually fall back to Earth as gravity wins and pulls the rocket back. If the rocket is given a larger amount of kinetic energy, sufficient for it to exceed the speed required to escape from the Earth, the rocket will leave the Earth altogether and travel out into space.

As with the rocket, so with the Universe. The balancing act here is between the energy of the expansion of the Universe (the kinetic energy) and the gravitational energy of all the matter in the Universe. The situation is summarized in Figure 12.2. If the energy of the expansion is sufficient to overcome the gravitational pull, then the Universe will continue expanding forever — such a Universe is known as 'open'. If, on the other hand, the energy of expansion is not enough to overcome the gravitational pull, the expansion will gradually slow down, and ultimately reverse — such a Universe is known as 'closed'.

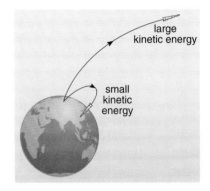

Figure 12.1 Possibilities for the path of a rocket launched from the Earth's surface.

12.1 A closed Universe

A **closed Universe** is one in which gravity wins; it is *finite* in size at all times. The expansion that is currently observed would gradually slow down and eventually stop all together. This corresponds to the maximum separation shown for the closed Universe in Figure 12.2. But gravity doesn't give up there! The expansion would then *reverse* — all the matter in the Universe would begin to converge as the Universe contracts. The contraction would gradually accelerate and all the galaxies and clusters would rush towards each other.

During the contraction, all the processes outlined Section 11 and in Activity 11.1 would follow in reverse order! The atoms would ionize under the impact of radiation; then the nuclei would be smashed apart into protons and neutrons; finally the nucleons themselves would disintegrate into their constituent quarks. Photons would spontaneously create pairs of particles and antiparticles until equal amounts of radiation and matter again filled the Universe. As the temperature of the contracting Universe rose, so the four interactions would each in turn become indistinguishable as the unifications proceeded in reverse order.

Ultimately things would reach a mirror image of the Big Bang — known as a 'big crunch'. And what would happen next? Well, one possibility is that's the end of everything — no more matter, no more space, no more time. The Universe just ends.

But maybe not … Some cosmologists suggest that what happens instead is a kind of 'big bounce'. At the very last instant, the whole sequence would turn around and a new Big Bang would happen. There would be a whole new period of expansion and contraction, repeating the history of the Universe again and again, over and over, for ever more. What we know as *the* Big Bang may simply be the latest in an infinite series of big bounces that is set to repeat an infinite number of times.

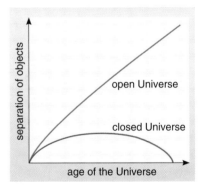

Figure 12.2 The way in which separations between objects vary with time in open and closed Universes. An open Universe expands forever, and so separations between clusters of galaxies continually increase. A closed Universe eventually begins to contract, whereupon the separations between clusters of galaxies would reduce.

12.2 An open Universe

An **open Universe** is one in which gravity loses, so that the separation between objects continues to increase for ever; it is *infinite* in size at all times. The first thing that would happen in such an ever-expanding Universe is that all the stars would run out of nuclear fuel and evolve into various types of 'dead' stars known as white dwarfs, neutron stars, and black holes. These 'dead' stars, along with any planets and other pieces of rock and dust, would gradually spiral in towards the centres of their respective galaxies where they would be consumed by the massive black holes that most astronomers believe exist in all galaxies. So, at this point the Universe would be cold and dead containing nothing but black holes and cosmic background photons, but still continuing to expand.

You may think that this is the end of the story — but not so. The name black hole was given to these objects in the belief that nothing — not even light — can escape from them, so they would literally appear to be a black hole in space. But the British cosmologist Stephen Hawking has shown that black holes are not entirely black. By a neat trick of quantum physics, black holes will eventually 'evaporate' into a swarm of subatomic particles and antiparticles. The process, however, takes an extremely long time — a black hole with the mass of a whole galaxy will take about 10^{97} years to evaporate! But that's okay, since the Universe has an infinite time to expand in this scenario. These particles and antiparticles would eventually mutually annihilate each other, each pair creating photons of electromagnetic radiation. So, the *final* fate of an open Universe is that it contains just photons, and simply becomes more and more dilute as the expansion continues. This is known as the heat death of the Universe.

Question 12.1 Write a few sentences to summarize the main differences between the properties of a closed Universe and an open Universe. ◀

12.3 A compromise ...?

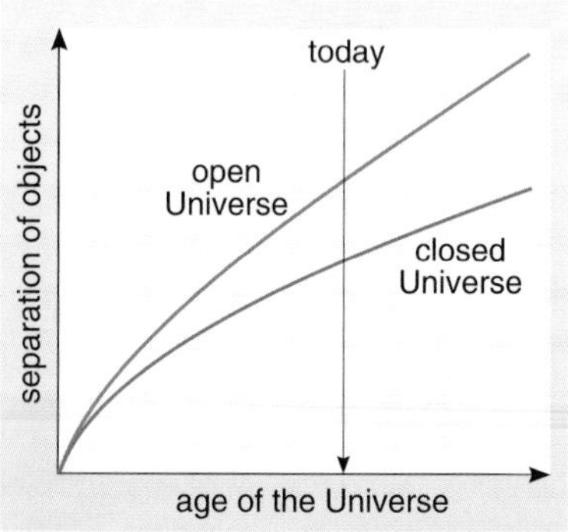

Unfortunately, from measurements alone, it is currently impossible to tell which type of Universe we inhabit. Figure 12.3 shows an enlarged view of part of Figure 12.2 corresponding to the period before a closed Universe would begin to contract. As you can see, at these 'early times' the expansion of both the open and closed Universes have very similar behaviour — in both cases the separation of objects is increasing, and the rate of expansion is slowing down. Current measurements of the rate at which the expansion of the Universe is slowing down are just not sufficiently accurate to distinguish between the possibilities. Note, however, that such measurements may become possible within the lifetime of this course. If you hear that cosmologists have measured the *deceleration parameter* of the Universe, this is what's happened.

⬤ What would happen to the rocket in Figure 12.1 if it were launched with insufficient kinetic energy to cause it to leave the Earth for good, but just enough to prevent it from falling back again?

⬤ The rocket would go into a stable orbit around the Earth.

By analogy with this, there is also a third possibility for the fate of the Universe — called by cosmologist John Barrow the 'British Compromise Universe'. This is a Universe that is not quite open, but not quite closed either. After all, if there are these two extremes there must be a critical situation in between the two in which the energy of expansion is *exactly* balanced by the gravitational pull. One proton more and gravity would win, leading to a big crunch; one proton less in this Universe and the

Figure 12.3 The behaviour of open and closed Universes at times before the closed Universe begins to contract. The rate of change of the expansion for both types of Universe is very similar.

expansion would win, leading to the heat death scenario. This Universe, more properly called a **flat Universe** model, is infinite in size at all times and has the interesting consequence that although the rate of expansion continues to slow down, it only reaches zero expansion rate at an infinite time in the future, at which point all objects in the Universe have an infinite separation.

Just which type of Universe we are in depends crucially on the mean density of matter in the Universe. The **critical density** is defined as that which corresponds to the flat Universe. If the Hubble constant is currently $60\,\mathrm{km\,s^{-1}\,Mpc^{-1}}$, then the critical density is currently $6.7 \times 10^{-27}\,\mathrm{kg\,m^{-3}}$, equivalent to about four protons per cubic metre. If the actual mean density is less than the critical value, the Universe is open, if the actual mean density is greater than the critical value, the Universe is closed.

⬤ A brief discussion relevant to the amount of matter in the Universe was first presented in Block 3. Can you remember what the rotation of galaxies tells us about the amount of matter in them?

◯ The way in which galaxies rotate tells us that there is more matter in their outer regions than can be seen directly as stars, gas, or dust. This matter only makes its presence felt by its gravitational interaction — it has mass — and is known as dark matter.

So, in the course so far you have met two types of matter in the Universe: visible matter that constitutes the gas, dust, stars and galaxies that we can actually see, and dark matter which makes its presence felt by the observed motion of stars in the outer regions of galaxies. Both visible and dark matter are believed to be composed of the familiar particles you have met throughout this block. Dark matter, as its name suggests, cannot be seen, but as we indicated in Block 3, there is probably 10 times more dark matter than visible matter in the Universe. It may be in the form of low mass dead stars, that were never able to undergo nuclear fusion, and which are situated in the halos of all galaxies. Searches for these 'massive compact halo objects' (known as MaCHOs for short), in the outer regions of our Galaxy are currently underway, and beginning to bear fruit.

Whatever form dark matter takes, by adding up all the visible matter and the (inferred) quantities of dark matter, cosmologists have calculated that the density of the Universe is around 10% of the critical density. Taken at face value this would indicate that we live in an open, ever-expanding Universe. But this is something of a puzzle. After all, why should the density of the Universe be *so close* to the critical value? You may think that 10% is not particularly close, but why is it not 10^{57} times smaller than the critical value, or 10^{38} times bigger than it, for instance? Such huge numbers are very common in cosmology, and at first sight there is no reason why our Universe should not have any density whatsoever.

One answer to this question is to say that, if the density of the Universe were very much larger than it is, then the gravitational attraction would have been so large that the Universe would have evolved and collapsed into a big crunch far too quickly for stars, planets and life to have formed. Conversely, if the density of the Universe were much smaller than it is, then the Universe would have expanded so quickly that gravitational attraction would not have been able to hold together galaxies and stars, or even allow them to form in the first place. Either way, it would be impossible for us to exist in such a Universe. The very fact that we are here to observe the Universe, constrains it to have some very special parameters.

A crucial result of Alan Guth's inflation theory, discussed in Section 11.3, is that the very rapid expansion drives the Universe to be very close to the critical divide between an open Universe and a closed Universe. Any deviations from the critical density that may have existed before inflation, are smoothed out by the inflationary process, resulting in a Universe with almost *exactly* the critical density, to an accuracy of better than one part in a million. In other words, if the inflation theory is correct, we live in an infinite flat Universe.

But, if this is indeed the case, you may be wondering where is the other 90% of the critical density that is so far unaccounted for by direct observations of visible matter and indirect observations of dark matter? This is the famous **missing mass** problem. Quite simply the implication is that about 90% of the Universe is made of some, so far unknown, constituents that may be totally unlike the rest of the protons, neutrons and electrons from which the familiar contents of the Universe are built. They are often referred to as 'weakly interacting massive particles' (or WIMPs for short) and they provide a suitably disconcerting thought on which to end the block!

Question 12.2 Write a few sentences summarizing what is meant by each of the following terms: (a) visible matter, (b) dark matter, (c) missing mass, in relation to the contents of the Universe. ◀

Activity 12.1 Science writing

In the Study File we have provided you with a recently published article which discusses aspects of cosmology and particle physics. This will allow you to apply the knowledge you have gained from Block 11 to understand a piece of science writing. Topics from Block 11 are often in the news, and after reading this block you should have a much greater appreciation of such news items in the future. ◀

Activity 12.2 New discoveries

Particle physics and cosmology are two areas where rapid progress is currently being made. This activity looks at recent developments in topics covered by this block. ◀

12.4 Summary of Section 12

There are three possibilities for the fate of the Universe. Just which type of Universe we are in depends crucially on the density of matter within it. If the density is greater than the critical density, the Universe is closed; if the density is less than the critical density, the Universe is open; if the density is equal to the critical density, the Universe is flat.

A closed Universe is finite in size. Gravity will eventually halt the expansion of such a Universe and then reverse it. The ultimate fate of a closed Universe is a big crunch in which it collapses, or a big bounce in which the whole cycle of expansion, contraction and crunch repeats.

An open Universe is infinite in size at all times. The expansion of such a Universe will continue into the infinite future. The entire matter content of an open Universe will eventually be consumed by massive black holes which ultimately evaporate in a stream of matter and antimatter particles. The final fate of an open Universe is an infinitely dilute sea of photons.

It is most probable that we live in a 'compromise' flat Universe in which the kinetic energy of expansion is exactly balanced by the gravitational energy of the matter within it. A flat Universe is also infinite in size at all times. A problem for this scenario is that it implies that at least 90% of the mass of the Universe is 'hidden' in the form of some new type of matter — the nature of which is presently unknown.

Questions: answers and comments

Question 1.1 In order from the smallest scale to the largest scale the terms are: planet, star, galaxy, cluster of galaxies.

A planet is a rocky or gaseous body (like the Earth or Jupiter, respectively) that orbits a star. Planets have only small internal energy sources and rely on their star to fuel processes happening on their surfaces or within their atmospheres.

A star is a ball of hydrogen and helium (like the Sun) which undergoes nuclear fusion within its core. The Sun has a family of planets, moons, asteroids and comets, all of which orbit around it. Other stars may also have planetary systems.

A galaxy is a collection of billions of stars, gravitationally bound together into either a flattened spiral or an elliptical shape. Our own spiral galaxy is called the Milky Way, or just the Galaxy.

Clusters of galaxies are again bound together by their mutual gravitational attraction. They can contain anything from a few dozen to a few thousand individual galaxies. The Local Group of galaxies, which contains the Milky Way and the Andromeda Galaxy, has only a few dozen members. It is probably part of a much larger 'super cluster'.

Question 2.1 From the information given in Box 2.1, you know that 1 pc = 3×10^{16} m. So the distance to the cluster can be converted into metres as follows:

$$200 \, \text{Mpc} = (200 \times 10^6) \times 1 \, \text{pc}$$

$$= (200 \times 10^6) \times (3 \times 10^{16}) \, \text{m} = 6 \times 10^{24} \, \text{m}$$

Question 2.2 (a) The circumference of a circle is given by $2\pi r$, which in this case is $2 \times \pi \times 5.00 \, \text{cm} = 31.4 \, \text{cm}$. The area of a circle is given by πr^2, which in this case is $\pi \times (5.00 \, \text{cm})^2 = 78.5 \, \text{cm}^2$. Note that the answers are given to three significant figures because the radius was given to three significant figures in the question (Block 2, Box 2.1).

(b) The surface area of a sphere is given by $4\pi r^2$, which in this case is $4 \times \pi \times (5.00 \, \text{cm})^2 = 314 \, \text{cm}^2$. The volume of a sphere is given by $\frac{4}{3}\pi r^3$, which in this case is $\frac{4}{3} \times \pi \times (5.00 \, \text{cm})^3 = 524 \, \text{cm}^3$.

Question 2.3 (a) If galaxy A were 25 times brighter than galaxy B, it would be $\sqrt{25} = 5$ times closer than galaxy B.

(b) If galaxy B were six times further away than galaxy A, it would appear to be $6^2 = 36$ times fainter than galaxy A.

Question 2.4 There are two ways of tackling this question. In the first method, using Equation 2.4, the brightness of the tenth brightest galaxy in one cluster divided by that of the tenth brightest galaxy in the other cluster is:

$$\frac{F_{\text{Perseus}}}{F_{\text{Corona}}} = \frac{1.0 \times 10^{-9} \, \text{W m}^{-2}}{7.2 \times 10^{-11} \, \text{W m}^{-2}} = 13.9$$

So the distances of the two clusters are given by:

$$\left(\frac{r_{\text{Corona}}}{r_{\text{Perseus}}}\right)^2 = \frac{F_{\text{Perseus}}}{F_{\text{Corona}}} = 13.9$$

$$\frac{r_{\text{Corona}}}{r_{\text{Perseus}}} = \sqrt{13.9} = 3.7$$

$$r_{\text{Corona}} = 3.7 \times r_{\text{Perseus}}$$

Therefore the Corona Borealis Cluster is at a distance of $3.7 \times 91 \, \text{Mpc} = 340 \, \text{Mpc}$ from the Earth. {Note this is a slightly different approach to that used in the question in the text. It shows that there are usually several ways of solving a numerical question.}

Alternatively, you could use the brightness and distance of the tenth brightest galaxy in the Perseus Cluster to determine its luminosity. Then, assuming this luminosity is also appropriate for the tenth brightest galaxy in the Corona Borealis Cluster, you could use the brightness of that galaxy to calculate the distance required. This would clearly involve the use of Equation 2.3 twice, and so the first method is far quicker.

Question 2.5 (a) Using Equation 2.6, the red-shift is given by $z = \dfrac{v}{c}$. So in this case we have

$$z = \frac{600 \, \text{m s}^{-1}}{3.0 \times 10^8 \, \text{m s}^{-1}} = 2.0 \times 10^{-6}$$

{Red-shift is a pure number and so has no units.}

(b) The shift in wavelength is the difference between the observed wavelength and the rest wavelength. This may be determined using Equation 2.5, which can be rearranged to give $\Delta\lambda = z \times \lambda_0$. So in this case, $\Delta\lambda = (2.0 \times 10^{-6} \times 656\,\text{nm}) = 1.3 \times 10^{-3}\,\text{nm}$. This is a tiny shift and for this reason the Doppler effect with light is not normally noticeable in everyday situations.

Question 2.6 (a) Since the wavelength of the light from the galaxy is shifted towards longer wavelengths, i.e. towards the red, the galaxy must be receding from the Earth.

(b) Using Equation 2.5,

$$z = \frac{\Delta\lambda}{\lambda_0}$$

so in this case

$$z = \frac{(500.7 - 486.1)\,\text{nm}}{486.1\,\text{nm}} = 0.030\,03$$

(c) Equation 2.6 states that $z = \dfrac{v}{c}$, and this can be rearranged to give $v = zc$. So here

$$v = 0.030\,03 \times 3.0 \times 10^8\,\text{m s}^{-1} = 9.009 \times 10^6\,\text{m s}^{-1}$$

or about $9\,000\,\text{km s}^{-1}$ to two significant figures.

Question 2.7 (a) The first step is to calculate the recession speed of the galaxy using Equation 2.7, $v = H_0 r$. Since H_0 is $60\,\text{km s}^{-1}\,\text{Mpc}^{-1}$ and the distance r is $400\,\text{Mpc}$, $v = (60\,\text{km s}^{-1}\,\text{Mpc}^{-1}) \times (400\,\text{Mpc}) = 2.4 \times 10^4\,\text{km s}^{-1}$.

The red-shift z of this galaxy can be found from Equation 2.6:

$$z = \frac{v}{c} = \frac{(2.4 \times 10^4\,\text{km s}^{-1})}{(3.0 \times 10^5\,\text{km s}^{-1})} = 0.08$$

(b) The first step is to calculate the recession speed of the galaxy using Equation 2.6, $z = \dfrac{v}{c}$. This can be rearranged as $v = z\,c$ and so in this case $v = 0.12 \times 3.0 \times 10^5\,\text{km s}^{-1} = 3.6 \times 10^4\,\text{km s}^{-1}$.

Then using Equation 2.7, $v = H_0 r$, the distance may be calculated as

$$r = \frac{v}{H_0} = \frac{3.6 \times 10^4\,\text{km s}^{-1}}{60\,\text{km s}^{-1}\,\text{Mpc}^{-1}} = 600\,\text{Mpc}$$

Question 2.8 Table 2.1 shows the values for the age of the Universe corresponding to various values for the Hubble constant. The age that you have determined should lie within the range included in the table. The important point to notice is that *larger* values of the Hubble constant correspond to *smaller* ages for the Universe.

Table 2.1 The age of the Universe corresponding to various values for the Hubble constant.

Hubble constant, H_0/km s^{-1} Mpc^{-1}	$t_0 = 1/H_0$ /10^{17} s	t_0/billion years	Age $= \frac{2}{3}t_0$ /billion years
20	16	50	33
30	10	31	21
40	7.8	24	16
45	6.8	21	14
50	6.2	19	13
55	5.6	18	12
60	5.3	17	11
65	4.7	15	10
70	4.4	14	9.3
75	4.0	13	8.7
80	3.9	12	8.0
90	3.4	11	7.3
100	3.1	9.7	6.5

Question 3.1 (a) From Figure 3.1 it can be estimated that an object at a temperature of $300\,\text{K}$ would radiate a black-body spectrum whose peak intensity occurs in the infrared region of the electromagnetic spectrum.

(b) From Figure 3.1 it may be estimated that an object whose black-body spectrum has a peak intensity in the X-ray part of the electromagnetic spectrum must be at a temperature of between about $10^6\,\text{K}$ and $10^9\,\text{K}$.

Question 3.2 Equation 3.1, $E_{\text{ph,mean}} = 2.7kT$, can be rearranged to make T the subject, namely $T = \dfrac{E_{\text{ph,mean}}}{2.7k}$. So in this case

$$T = \frac{(1.4\,\text{eV})}{(2.7 \times 8.6 \times 10^{-5}\,\text{eV K}^{-1})} = 6\,000\,\text{K}$$

This temperature is comparable to that in the Sun's outer atmosphere.

Question 3.3   The first step is to calculate the mean photon energy corresponding to 10^5 K. Using Equation 3.1, $E_{ph,mean} = 2.7kT$, in this case

$$E_{ph,mean} = 2.7 \times (8.6 \times 10^{-5}\,\text{eV K}^{-1}) \times (10^5\,\text{K}) = 23.2\,\text{eV}$$

{We write the answer to three significant figures at this stage, and will only round it to two significant figures at the final stage of the calculation.}

Next, the photon energy can be converted into a frequency using Equation 9.1 from Block 7, $E_{ph} = hf$. Making f the subject we have $f = \dfrac{E_{ph}}{h}$ which in this case gives

$$f = \frac{(23.2\,\text{eV})}{(4.1 \times 10^{-15}\,\text{eV Hz}^{-1})} = 5.66 \times 10^{15}\,\text{Hz}$$

{Again we retain three significant figures for the time being.}

Finally, the frequency can be converted into a wavelength using Equation 8.2 from Block 7, $c = f\lambda$. Making λ the subject we have $\lambda = \dfrac{c}{f}$ which in this case gives

$$\lambda = \frac{(3.0 \times 10^8\,\text{m s}^{-1})}{(5.66 \times 10^{15}\,\text{Hz})} = 5.30 \times 10^{-8}\,\text{m}$$

or about 53 nm (to two sig figs).

This corresponds to the ultraviolet part of the electromagnetic spectrum (which is in agreement with Figure 3.1).

Question 4.1   (a) Gravitational interactions are clearly important here: the attraction of every atom in the child's body, by every atom in the rest of the Earth, is responsible for slowing down the ascent and speeding up the descent. While bouncing, electromagnetic interactions come into play: they are responsible for holding together the atoms that form the child and the trampoline, and for the chemical processes by which the child converts energy in its muscles to replenish losses due to friction.

(b) Electromagnetic interactions are involved in the flow of electric current and the conversion of its energy into light in the lamp. They also govern the propagation of the light and its absorption by your retina. However, the electricity may have been generated in a nuclear power station, where both strong and weak interactions are involved in the nuclear reactor, or in a hydroelectric

power station, where gravitational energy of water is involved.

(c) As in (b), electromagnetic interactions are involved in the absorption of the radiation, and the subsequent chemical changes to the skin. The radiation was generated by electromagnetic processes in the Sun, but the ultimate power source was nuclear, involving both strong and weak interactions. Gravitational interactions hold the Sun together and hold the bather on the beach.

(d) Chemotherapy, as the name suggests, involves chemical processes, and hence the electromagnetic interactions of electrons. Radiotherapy may involve injecting radioactive 'tracers', entailing strong and weak interactions in nuclei.

{Don't worry if you didn't identify the subsidiary interactions in each case.}

Question 5.1   (a) Setting $Q_1 = -e$ and $Q_2 = e$ in Equation 5.1, we obtain

$$F_e = -k_e \frac{(-e \times e)}{r^2} = \frac{k_e e^2}{r^2}$$
$$= \frac{(8.988 \times 10^9\,\text{N m}^2\,\text{C}^{-2}) \times (1.602 \times 10^{-19}\,\text{C})^2}{(5.29 \times 10^{-11}\,\text{m})^2}$$
$$= 8.24 \times 10^{-8}\,\text{N}$$

(b) The force you found in (a), 8.24×10^{-8} N, has an order of magnitude of 10^{-7} N. Now, the weight of a grain of sand of mass m is given by $F_g = mg$ (Block 5). Using $g = 10$ m s^{-2}, and noting that 1 mg $= 10^{-6}$ kg, we obtain the weight of the grain of sand as $F_g = (10^{-6}\,\text{kg}) \times (10\,\text{m s}^{-1}) = 10^{-5}$ N. This is only two orders of magnitude larger than the electric force between an electron and a proton.

Question 5.2   We define $\alpha_{em} = 2\pi \dfrac{k_e e^2}{hc}$ (Equation 5.2). The extraterrestrial constant is $\dfrac{hc}{k_e e^2}$. The only difference is the factor of 2π and the fact that the extraterrestrial constant is the inverse of ours. So their constant is equal to $\dfrac{2\pi}{\alpha_{em}}$. Our value for their constant is $2\pi \times (137.036\,00 \pm 0.000\,01) = 861.022\,58 \pm 0.000\,6$. Theirs is $861.022\,6 \pm 0.000\,1$. The uncertainties in the two answers overlap, i.e. the range of values encompassed by $861.022\,58 \pm 0.000\,6$, and the range of values encompassed by $861.022\,6 \pm 0.000\,1$ include some of the same values. So the strength of electromagnetic interactions is the same in their part of the Universe as ours, to an accuracy of 1 part in 10 million.

Question 5.3   Rearranging Equation 5.3, we obtain $k_m = \dfrac{F_m r}{2 I_1 I_2 L}$. The units of the right-hand side of this equation are: $\dfrac{N \times m}{A \times A \times m}$. The metres cancel, hence the SI unit of k_m is $\dfrac{N}{A^2}$, i.e. $N\,A^{-2}$. Equivalently, since $1\,A = 1\,C\,s^{-1}$, this may be written as $N\,(C\,s^{-1})^{-2}$, i.e. $N\,s^2\,C^{-2}$. {It is conventional to list the positive powers before the negative powers in such combinations of units.}

Question 5.4   (a) To remove its sag, the current in the thin wire must be opposite in direction to that in the metal bar, i.e. the current in the wire must be flowing from right to left. Then the magnetic force is repulsive and acts upwards on the thin wire, countering its weight.

(b) The magnetic force on a 10 m length of wire which is 0.5 cm (or 0.005 m) from the bar is given by Equation 5.3 as

$$F_m = k_m \frac{2 I_1 I_2 L}{r}$$

$$= 1 \times 10^{-7}\,N\,A^{-2} \times \frac{2 \times 5\,A \times 200\,A \times 10\,m}{0.005\,m}$$

$$= 0.4\,N$$

This balances the weight of that length of wire, so clearly $F_m = F_g$. The weight of the wire is given by $F_g = mg$, so its mass is given by

$$m = \frac{F_m}{g} = \frac{0.4\,N}{10\,m\,s^{-2}} = 0.04\,kg \text{ or } 40\,g$$

Question 5.5   (a) Dividing one constant by the other (remember k_m is *exactly* $1 \times 10^{-7}\,N\,s^2\,C^{-2}$) we get

$$\frac{k_e}{k_m} = \frac{8.988 \times 10^9\,N\,m^2\,C^{-2}}{1 \times 10^{-7}\,N\,s^2\,C^{-2}}$$

$$= 8.988 \times 10^{16}\,m^2\,s^{-2}$$

which is independent of the definition of either the coulomb or the newton.

(b) The unit of this value is clearly that of (speed)^2, i.e. $(m\,s^{-1})^2$. The one universal constant of nature that has been encountered in this course with the unit of speed is the speed of light $c = 2.998 \times 10^8\,m\,s^{-1}$. The value calculated in part (a) is in fact identical to c^2. {As will be explained in Section 5.3, this is no accident!}

Question 5.6   (a) With $\Delta E = 10^6\,eV$, the maximum time by which the energy debt must be repaid is given by $1\,MeV \times t = h$. Therefore

$$t = \frac{h}{1\,MeV} = \frac{4.1 \times 10^{-15}\,eV\,s}{10^6\,eV} = 4.1 \times 10^{-21}\,s$$

{This is an incredibly short time-scale — only a few thousandths of a billionth of a billionth of a second!}

(b) The energy debt could be repaid by the electron and positron annihilating each other.

Question 5.7   (a) The time obtained in the answer to Question 5.6 is $t = 4.1 \times 10^{-21}$ s. The distance over which the strength of the electromagnetic interaction is increased is given by the speed of light multiplied by the time interval, i.e. $r = ct = (3.0 \times 10^8\,m\,s^{-1}) \times (4.1 \times 10^{-21}\,s) = 1.2 \times 10^{-12}\,m$, or about $10^{-12}\,m$ to the nearest order of magnitude.

(b) Since the typical separation of an electron and a proton in a hydrogen atom is of the order of 10^{-10} m, this is about 1% of that distance.

Question 6.1   (a) The electric force of repulsion between two up quarks is given by

$$F_e = -\frac{k_e Q^2}{r^2}$$

The electric charge of an up quark is $+\frac{2}{3}e$, or $(\frac{2}{3} \times 1.6 \times 10^{-19})\,C$, which is of the order of $10^{-19}\,C$. The Coulomb constant is of the order of $10^{10}\,N\,m^2\,C^{-2}$. Substituting these values we therefore obtain

$$F_e = -\frac{(10^{10}\,N\,m^2\,C^{-2}) \times (10^{-19}\,C)^2}{(10^{-15}\,m)^2}$$

$$= -\frac{10^{10} \times 10^{-38}}{10^{-30}}\,N = -\frac{10^{-28}}{10^{-30}}\,N$$

$$= -10^{-28+30}\,N = -10^2\,N$$

So two up quarks will feel an electric force of repulsion of about 100 N.

(b) Since the strong force at this separation has a magnitude of 10^5 N, the electric force of repulsion is only about one-thousandth of the strong force of attraction, when acting on the two quarks inside a nucleon.

Question 6.2 An available energy of 100 GeV corresponds to 10^{11} eV. Converting this into joules, we get $(10^{-19} \times 10^{11})$ J = 10^{-8} J. From Block 5, the work done is equal to the force applied multiplied by the distance moved, $W = Fd$. In this case, the work done is the available energy, so, working against a force of strength $F = 10^5$ N, this energy is sufficient only to achieve a separation

$$d = \frac{W}{F} = \frac{10^{-8}\,\text{J}}{10^5\,\text{N}} = 10^{-13}\,\text{m}$$

This distance is about one hundred times the size of a proton, 10^{-15} m.

Question 6.3 To get four jets of hadrons, we need the radiation of two gluons. By analogy with the example in the question, this decreases the probability by a factor $\alpha_s^2 = (0.12 \times 0.12) = 10^{-2}$, at an energy of 100 GeV.

Question 6.4 Table 6.2 is the completed version of Table 6.1. Only particles with non-zero electric charge interact with photons. Only particles with colour charge interact with gluons.

Question 7.1 (a) As shown by the Feynman diagram in Figure 7.3a, β^+-decay involves an up quark (u) changing into a down quark (d), at A, where a W^+ boson is created. Shortly thereafter, the energy account is balanced, at B, by the production of a positron (e^+) and an electron neutrino (ν_e).

The electric charge initially is that of an up quark, i.e. $+\frac{2}{3}e$. The products of the decay are a down quark (electric charge, $-\frac{1}{3}e$), a positron (electric charge, $+e$) and an electron neutrino (electric charge, 0). The net electric charge after the decay is therefore $-\frac{1}{3}e + e = +\frac{2}{3}e$, the same as it was initially. Electric charge is therefore conserved.

There is one quark present both before and after the decay, so the total number of quarks minus the number of antiquarks is conserved, and equal to one. There are no leptons present initially, but one lepton (the electron neutrino) and one antilepton (the positron) present at the end. Therefore the total number of leptons minus the number of antileptons is also conserved, and equal to zero.

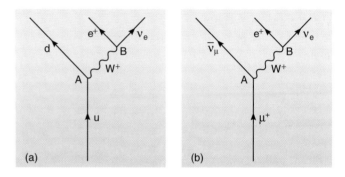

Figure 7.3 Feynman diagrams showing (a) a β^+-decay process in which an up quark converts into a down quark, and (b) the decay of an antimuon.

Table 6.2 Completed version of Table 6.1. The properties of the fundamental consituents of the world.

Particle	Electric charge	Colour charge	Quanta with which the particle interacts
electron	$-e$	–	photons
electron neutrino	0	–	–
up quark	$+\frac{2}{3}e$	red, green or blue	photons, gluons
down quark	$-\frac{1}{3}e$	red, green or blue	photons, gluons
photon	0	–	–
gluon	0	colour and anticolour	gluons

(b) The Feynman diagram in Figure 7.3b shows how a W^+ boson is involved in the decay

$$\mu^+ \longrightarrow e^+ + \nu_e + \bar{\nu}_\mu$$

At A the antimuon (μ^+) decays to a W^+ boson and a muon antineutrino $\bar{\nu}_\mu$, then at B the W^+ boson decays into a positron (e^+) and an electron neutrino (ν_e).

The electric charge initially is that of an antimuon, i.e. $+e$. The products of the decay are a positron (electric charge, $+e$), a muon antineutrino (electric charge, 0) and an electron neutrino (electric charge, 0). The net electric charge after the decay is therefore $+e$, the same as it was initially. Electric charge is therefore conserved.

There are no quarks or antiquarks involved in this decay, so the number of quarks is conserved, and equal to zero. There is one antilepton present initially (the antimuon), and two antileptons (the positron and muon antineutrino) plus one lepton (the electron neutrino) present at the end. Therefore the total number of leptons is also conserved, and equal to one.

Question 7.2   The fraction of neutrons remaining after one half-life is $\frac{1}{2}$; the fraction that remain after two half-lives is $\left(\frac{1}{2} \times \frac{1}{2}\right) = \frac{1}{2^2}$; in general the fraction that remain after n half-lives is $\frac{1}{2^n}$. So if we know the value of n, we can find the fraction, and then number of nuclei, remaining.

(a) In 30 s, 30 half-lives elapse, so the fraction of neutrons remaining is $\frac{1}{2^{30}}$. Using a calculator to work this out, gives 9×10^{-10} or about 10^{-9} to the nearest order of magnitude. So the number of neutrons remaining after 30 s is $10^{68} \times 10^{-9} = 10^{59}$. {The mass of these neutrons is equivalent to a mass about one hundred times that of the Sun.}

(b) In three minutes, or 180 s, 180 half-lives elapse, so the fraction of neutrons remaining is $\frac{1}{2^{180}}$. Using a calculator to work this out, gives 7×10^{-55} or about 10^{-54} to the nearest order of magnitude. So the number of neutrons remaining after three minutes is $10^{68} \times 10^{-54} = 10^{14}$. {The mass of these neutrons is roughly equivalent to the mass of a single biological cell.}

Question 7.3   The strength of the electromagnetic interaction *increases* with increasing energy. At low energies (well below 1 GeV) it is characterized by $\alpha_{em} = \frac{1}{137}$, at 100 GeV its strength increases to $\alpha_{em} = \frac{1}{128}$.

The strength of the strong interaction *decreases* with increasing energy. At 1 GeV it is characterized by $\alpha_s = 0.4$ (from Figure 6.7) whereas at 100 GeV its strength has fallen to $\alpha_s = 0.12$.

The strength of the weak interaction *increases* with increasing energy. At 100 GeV its strength is comparable to that of the electromagnetic interaction, $\alpha_w = 10^{-2}$, whereas at an energy of 1 GeV, it is a factor of 10^8 smaller, $\alpha_w = 10^{-10}$.

Question 8.1   (a) Setting $m_1 = m_p$ and $m_2 = m_e$ in Equation 8.1, we obtain

$$F_g = \frac{Gm_p m_e}{r^2}$$
$$= \frac{(6.672 \times 10^{-11}) \times (1.673 \times 10^{-27}) \times (9.110 \times 10^{-31})}{(5.29 \times 10^{-11})^2} \text{ N}$$
$$= 3.63 \times 10^{-47} \text{ N (to three sig figs)}$$

(b) The electric force between a proton and an electron at this separation is 8.24×10^{-8} N (from the answer to Question 5.1), which is about 10^{39} times larger than the gravitational force.

Question 8.2   Equations 8.1 and 8.3 both give expressions for the gravitational force of attraction. We can equate them, providing that we identify m_2 and r in Equation 8.1 with the mass and radius of the Earth, respectively. So, equating Equation 8.1 with 8.3 and using r_{Earth} and m_{Earth} for the Earth's radius and mass, we have:

$$F_g = G\frac{m_1 m_{Earth}}{r_{Earth}^2} = m_1 g$$

The mass m_1 cancels out from both sides of this equation leaving:

$$G\frac{m_{Earth}}{r_{Earth}^2} = g$$

which may be rearranged to make the mass of the Earth the subject of the equation:

$$m_{Earth} = \frac{gr_{Earth}^2}{G}$$
$$= \frac{(9.8 \, m \, s^{-2}) \times (6.4 \times 10^6 \, m)^2}{6.7 \times 10^{-11} \, N \, m^2 \, kg^{-2}}$$
$$= 6.0 \times 10^{24} \, kg$$

{Since the radius of the Earth, the acceleration due to gravity and the gravitational constant can all be measured, here is a practical means of determining the mass of the planet Earth.}

Question 8.3 Newton's law of gravity was phrased in terms of a force between massive particles. A quantum theory of gravity will describe gravitational interactions in terms of the exchange of gravitons.

Question 9.1 The mass of four protons is $4 \times 0.938 \, GeV/c^2 = 3.752 \, GeV/c^2$, whereas the mass of a single helium nucleus is $3.727 \, GeV/c^2$. The helium nucleus has about $0.025 \, GeV/c^2$ or $25 \, MeV/c^2$ *less* mass than the four protons from which it was built. This missing mass appears as the mass of the positrons in Step 1 (about $0.5 \, MeV/c^2$ each), the energy of the γ-ray in Step 2, and as the extra kinetic energy of all the products, at each stage.

Question 9.2 (a) Only the first step of the reaction chain described in Section 9.2 depends on the weak interaction. The weak interaction allows one type of quark to convert into another when W bosons are emitted. In Step 1, two protons are fused together to make a deuterium nucleus consisting of one proton and one neutron, with the emission of a positron and a neutrino. The net effect is that a proton has been converted into a neutron, a positron and a neutrino. At a deeper level, an up quark transforms into a down quark and emits a W^+ boson. This then decays into a positron and an electron neutrino. As you saw in Section 7 (Figure 7.3a), this involves the weak interaction.

(b) All three steps in the reaction chain rely on the strong interaction. In each case, positively charged particles (protons and nuclei) are fused together. This entails that their electrical repulsion be overcome, and the residual strong interaction that operates inside nuclei is the only one of the four fundamental interactions which is able to do this.

Question 9.3 (a) In the case of free–free emission, the change in energy of the electron can take *any* value, up to the kinetic energy that the electron initially possesses. So, the photon emitted in the process can similarly have any energy. By contrast, in bound–bound emission, only certain energy levels are allowed for the atom. So the photon emitted can have only certain specific energies.

(b) Summing over many such events, the first process would give rise to a continuous spectrum of photon energies, whilst the second process would give rise to an emission line spectrum.

Question 10.1 (a) The completed Table 10.1 is shown in Table 10.2.

Table 10.2 Completed version Table 10.1. Quanta involved in electroweak unification.

Quanta	Mass/$\frac{GeV}{c^2}$
photon	0
W^+ boson	80
W^- boson	80
Z^0 boson	90
Higgs boson	1 000

(b) The photon is the only one that is massless. As a consequence of this, Coulomb's law is an inverse square law of force with a very large range. Conversely, W and Z bosons do have mass and so have only a very short range.

Question 10.2 (a) About 13 orders of magnitude span the more or less reliable parts of the story of Blocks 7 and 11: from the 1 eV energy transfers in hydrogen atoms, to the 10^{13} eV (10^4 GeV) investigated at existing or planned particle accelerators.

(b) A further 11 orders of magnitude remain in the range up to a notional scale of 10^{24} eV (10^{15} GeV) conjectured for grand unification.

Question 10.3 (a) The value of the Planck mass is:

$$M_{Pl} = \sqrt{\frac{(6.6 \times 10^{-34} \, J \, s) \times (3.0 \times 10^8 \, m \, s^{-1})}{2\pi \times (6.7 \times 10^{-11} \, N \, m^2 \, kg^{-2})}}$$
$$= 2.2 \times 10^{-8} \, kg$$

{This is about 10^{19} times larger than the mass of a proton.}

(b) The value of the Planck energy, in joules, is given by

$$E_{Pl} = (2.2 \times 10^{-8} \, \text{kg}) \times (3.0 \times 10^8 \, \text{m s}^{-1})^2$$
$$= 2.0 \times 10^9 \, \text{J}$$

Converting this energy into electronvolts gives:

$$E_{Pl} = \frac{2.0 \times 10^9 \, \text{J}}{1.6 \times 10^{-19} \, \text{J eV}^{-1}} = 1.3 \times 10^{28} \, \text{eV}$$

Since $1 \, \text{GeV} = 10^9 \, \text{eV}$, the Planck energy is therefore about $10^{19} \, \text{GeV}$.

(c) This exceeds the conjectured scale of $10^{15} \, \text{GeV}$ for grand unification by another four orders of magnitude.

Question 10.4   (a) Higgs bosons, (b) X bosons, (c) strings.

{Watch out for mention of these three topics in the news media in the next few years.}

Question 11.1   (a) Section 2 concluded that the separations between distant objects are continually *increasing* with time. Section 3 concluded that the temperature of the Universe is continually *decreasing* with time.

(b) This implies that the early Universe was much *denser* and *hotter* than it is today.

Question 11.2   (a) Up quarks have an electric charge of $+\frac{2}{3}e$, down quarks have a charge of $-\frac{1}{3}e$, electrons have a charge of $-e$, and neutrinos have zero charge. Antimatter counterparts of each of these have the opposite charge. In order to balance charge in each case shown, the X bosons must have a charge of $+\frac{1}{3}e$.

{In fact X bosons come in two varieties, one, as we have seen has a charge of $+\frac{1}{3}e$, and the other variety of X boson, which decays differently, has a charge of $+\frac{4}{3}e$.}

(b) The equivalent decays of antimatter X bosons would be:

$$\overline{X} \longrightarrow \overline{u} + \overline{d}$$

$$\overline{X} \longrightarrow u + e^-$$

$$\overline{X} \longrightarrow d + \nu_e$$

As with other particles, antimatter X bosons have opposite charge to matter X bosons. The antimatter X bosons above therefore have a charge of $-\frac{1}{3}e$.

{The second variety of antimatter X boson has a charge of $-\frac{4}{3}e$.}

Question 11.3   In a non-expanding Universe, the horizon distance is simply the speed of light multiplied by the age of the Universe, (distance = speed × time). Converting the age into seconds, the age of the Universe is $(10^{10} \, \text{years}) \times (3 \times 10^7 \, \text{seconds per year}) = 3 \times 10^{17} \, \text{s}$. So the horizon distance is $(3 \times 10^8 \, \text{m s}^{-1}) \times (3 \times 10^{17} \, \text{s}) = 10^{26} \, \text{m}$ to the nearest order of magnitude.

Question 11.4   The region of space that was destined to expand to become the currently observable Universe must have been a factor of 3×10^{27} smaller than it is now. This corresponds to a radius of

$$\frac{3 \times 10^{26} \, \text{m}}{3 \times 10^{27}} = 10^{-1} \, \text{m or } 10 \, \text{cm}$$

Question 11.5   (a) In the non-inflationary model, the horizon distance at early times was much *smaller* than the radius of the region of space that was destined to become the currently observable Universe. In the inflationary model, the horizon distance at early times was much *larger* than the radius of the region of space that was destined to become the currently observable Universe.

(b) The non-inflationary model predicts that the radius of the currently observable Universe today is *equal* to the horizon distance. In contrast, the inflationary model predicts that the horizon distance is greater than the radius of the currently observable Universe today, thanks to the vast increase in scale accumulated during the period of inflation.

Question 11.6   (a) As mentioned in Block 7 Section 6, the third generation quarks (t and b) are more massive than the second generation quarks (c and s) which in turn are more massive than the first generation quarks (u and d). Only upper limits to the masses of neutrinos are known, but tauons are more massive than muons which in turn are more massive than electrons.

(b) As summarized at the end of Section 8 of this block, only quarks take part in strong interactions. All quarks and leptons participate in weak interactions. All electrically charged particles experience electromagnetic interactions.

(c) As discussed in Block 7 Section 6, antimatter particles have the opposite electric charge, but the same mass, as their matter counterparts. {As noted in Section 6 of this block, antimatter quarks also have the opposite colour charge to matter quarks.}

Question 11.7 Feynman diagrams for these decay processes are shown in Figure 11.10.

(a) Figure 11.10a shows the decay of a charm quark into a strange quark and a W^+ boson, which in turn decays into a positron and an electron neutrino.

(b) Figure 11.10b shows the decay of a strange quark into an up quark and a W^- boson, which in turn decays into an electron and an electron antineutrino.

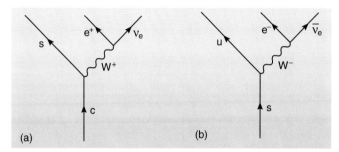

(a) (b)

Figure 11.10 Feynman diagrams illustrating the decay of (a) a charm quark and (b) a strange quark.

Question 11.8 A neutron is composed of two down quarks and an up quark, whilst a proton is composed of two up quarks and a down quark. The process may therefore be represented as

$$d \longrightarrow u + e^- + \bar{v}_e$$

This process may also be represented by the Feynman diagram shown in Figure 11.11. A down quark transforms to an up quark and emits a W^- boson. The W^- boson then decays into an electron and an electron antineutrino.

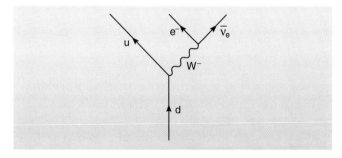

Figure 11.11 A Feynman diagram indicating the weak process underlying the decay of a neutron.

This process is a manifestation of the weak interaction since it involves the transformation of a down quark into an up quark plus a lepton and an antilepton. All processes which involve quarks changing flavour, with the emission of lepton–antilepton pairs, are weak interactions.

Question 11.9 Section 9.2 states that the first stage of the proton–proton chain

$$p + p \longrightarrow {}^2_1 H + e^+ + v_e$$

relies on the weak interaction and takes, on average, 10^{10} years to occur for any individual pair of protons. In the early Universe at this epoch, there was just not enough time for this reaction to occur to any great extent over the period considered here. {Instead, deuterium nuclei were able to form via Equation 11.7, which does not occur in the Sun as it contains no free neutrons — in the Sun essentially all the neutrons are bound up in helium nuclei.}

Question 11.10 In principle you could combine ${}^2_1 H$ with ${}^3_2 He$, or you could combine a proton with ${}^4_2 He$. Both of these would give a nucleus consisting of three protons and two neutrons: ${}^5_3 Li$. This is unstable as it has too many protons, and splits apart into ${}^4_2 He$ plus a proton. Alternatively, you might try adding a free neutron to a ${}^4_2 He$ nucleus to make ${}^5_2 He$, but this too is unstable as it contains too many neutrons, and splits apart again. What ever combination you might try, there really is no stable nucleus with a mass number of five. {Refer back to the CD-ROM activity 'Nucleons in nuclei' in Block 7 if necessary.}

Question 11.11 (a) One way to calculate the answer is as follows. Imagine that you have a box containing 14 protons and 2 neutrons — the 7 : 1 ratio mentioned in the question. If a nucleus of helium-4 is made from 2 protons and 2 neutrons, there will be 12 protons remaining in the box, each of which can be considered as a hydrogen nucleus. Therefore there are 12 hydrogen nuclei for every one helium-4 nucleus in the Universe.

(b) Taking the mass of a helium-4 nucleus to be four units, and that of a hydrogen nucleus to be one unit, the relative masses of the helium-4 and hydrogen in the box are 4 and 12, respectively. The fraction of the mass in the box due to helium-4 is therefore $\frac{4}{4+12} = 0.25$ or 25%, and that due to hydrogen is $\frac{12}{4+12} = 0.75$ or 75%. {In fact the actual mass fraction of helium-4 that is predicted to have come out of the Big Bang is between about 22% and 24%.}

Question 11.12 (a) Equation 11.2 shows that a single matter X boson will decay to produce either two quarks (q) or an antiquark ($\bar{q}$) plus antilepton ($\bar{l}$). So according to the question, the matter X bosons will decay as follows:

$$1\,000\,000\,012X \longrightarrow 1\,000\,000\,012q + 1\,000\,000\,012q$$

$$1\,000\,000\,000X \longrightarrow 1\,000\,000\,000\bar{q} + 1\,000\,000\,000\bar{l}$$

In contrast, a single antimatter X boson will decay into either two antiquarks ($\bar{q}$) or a quark (q) and a lepton (l). So the antimatter X bosons will decay as follows:

$$1\,000\,000\,012\overline{X} \longrightarrow 1\,000\,000\,012q + 1\,000\,000\,012l$$

$$1\,000\,000\,000\overline{X} \longrightarrow 1\,000\,000\,000\bar{q} + 1\,000\,000\,000\bar{q}$$

Adding up the totals, it can be seen that this region of the Universe now consists of 3 000 000 036 quarks, 3 000 000 000 antiquarks, 1 000 000 012 leptons, 1 000 000 000 antileptons and the original 4 000 000 000 photons.

(b) Next we can assume that all the antimatter particles annihilate with an equal number of matter particles. Each annihilation will produce two photons, so a total of 8 000 000 000 more photons are created, as follows:

$$3\,000\,000\,000\bar{q} + 3\,000\,000\,000q \longrightarrow 6\,000\,000\,000\gamma$$

$$1\,000\,000\,000\bar{l} + 1\,000\,000\,000l \longrightarrow 2\,000\,000\,000\gamma$$

This region of the Universe now contains 12 000 000 000 photons (the four billion originally present plus the eight billion created by the annihilation reactions), as well as just 36 quarks and 12 leptons.

(c) If we assume that 18 of the quarks are up quarks and 18 are down quarks, then this is sufficient to make 6 protons and 6 neutrons, as follows:

$$6u + 6u + 6d \longrightarrow 6p$$

$$6d + 6d + 6u \longrightarrow 6n$$

(d) Since we can assume that of the 12 leptons, 6 are electrons and 6 are electron neutrinos, the fate of this region of the Universe is that it will consist of just twelve baryons (6p and 6n), twelve leptons ($6e^-$ and $6v_e$) plus twelve billion photons. As mentioned in the text, this relative proportion of one baryon per billion photons is what is observed in our Universe today.

Question 11.13 (a) Nucleosynthesis — the formation of nuclei — occurred in the early Universe, between about 100 and 1 000 seconds after the Big Bang. During this epoch, only low mass nuclei, such as deuterium, helium and lithium were formed. A second site for nucleosynthesis is in the heart of stars, like the Sun. Here, hydrogen undergoes nuclear fusion to form helium, and later on helium can fuse to form carbon, oxygen, silicon and other (relatively) low mass nuclei. In fact, most nuclei below an atomic mass of about 62 (nuclei up to iron, cobalt and nickel) can form in the heart of stars in this way. Finally, nucleosynthesis can occur at the end of a star's life during a supernova explosion. In this process, many nuclei more massive than iron are formed and thrown violently out into the Universe, where they can be incorporated into future generations of stars and planets.

(b)(i) Most of the helium nuclei were formed during the primordial nucleosynthesis, soon after the Big Bang.

(ii) Most of the oxygen nuclei were formed in the heart of stars.

(iii) All the uranium nuclei were formed as a result of supernova explosions.

Question 11.14 Perhaps the simplest way to decide in which order a sequence of events occurred is to think about the energy required for each process. If the processes are then arranged in descending order of energy, they will automatically be in a time-ordered sequence.

Clearly, the formation of the fundamental constituents of matter, quarks and leptons, require the most energy of these processes. This event must have occurred first. Next, as the energy dropped, quarks and antiquarks would have mutually annihilated, leaving behind the relatively few residual matter particles from which to construct the material content of the Universe. Protons and neutrons form next, from the residual quarks. When neutrinos cease to interact with matter, the equilibrium conversion between protons and neutrons effectively stops. After this, the electrons and positrons mutually annihilate leaving relatively few electrons to balance the charge of the protons. From this point on, light nuclei are able to form from the protons and neutrons available. Atoms form next from the nuclei and electrons that now constitute the matter content of the Universe. Finally background photons interact for the last time with matter when the Universe is about 300 000 years old.

The sequence of the processes listed in the question is therefore:

(iii) the formation of quarks and leptons

(vi) the annihilation of quarks and antiquarks

(iv) the formation of protons and neutrons

(vii) neutrinos cease to interact with matter or radiation

(v) the annihilation of electrons and positrons

(ii) the formation of light nuclei

(i) the formation of atoms

(viii) background photons cease to interact with matter

Question 11.15   The three key pieces of observational evidence for the hot big bang are:

> the Hubble relationship linking the speed and distance of distant galaxies;
>
> the cosmic microwave background radiation;
>
> the relative abundances of helium, lithium and other light elements.

The first galaxies formed when the Universe was at least a few hundred thousand years old, and possibly much later. So, in theory, observations of distant galaxies only allow cosmologists to reach back this far in time.

The cosmic background radiation last interacted with matter when the Universe was about 300 000 years old. So observations of it only let cosmologists investigate conditions at that epoch.

It is the relative abundances of the light elements that allow cosmologists to reach back the furthest. These elements were formed when the Universe was between 100 and 1 000 seconds old, and the reactions which created them were sensitive to things like the ratio of neutrons to protons, which were determined even earlier.

Question 12.1   A closed Universe is finite in size and will eventually stop expanding. From here on a closed Universe will contract, ultimately reaching a big crunch, or a big bounce in which the whole sequence repeats. An open Universe is infinite in size and will carry on expanding forever.

Question 12.2   (a) Visible matter is the material in the Universe that we can actually see with telescopes. It is made up of familiar protons, neutrons and electrons and constitutes the galaxies, stars, gas and dust that we 'see' as a result of the light and other electromagnetic radiation they emit.

(b) Dark matter is invisible, but it too is probably made up of protons, neutrons and electrons. It is dark because it emits no light, or other radiation. It is thought to exist in the outer regions (or halos) of galaxies and may be made up of 'dead stars' that were never able to undergo nuclear fusion. These dead stars are referred to as MaCHOs.

(c) Missing mass is the matter that is predicted to exist if the Universe really does have a critical density. It cannot be made up of familiar protons, neutrons and electrons. Not only is it invisible, but we have no real idea what it is made of. These unknown particles are called WIMPs.

Acknowledgements

Grateful acknowledgement is made to the following sources for permission to reproduce material in this block:

Figures

Figure 1.1: W. M. Keck Observatory; *Figure 1.2:* CERN Photo; *Figure 2.4:* NASA and AURA/STScI; *Figure 2.7:* Courtesy of Patrick Gorvan; *Figure 3.2:* Danish History of Science Picture Archive; *Figure 3.3:* Corporate Archives/Lucent Technologies/Bell Laboratories; *Figure 5.1:* Versailles et Trianon Lecomte-Vernet, portrait du Physicien Charles Auguste de Coulomb, © Photo Reunion des Musees Nationaux; *Figure 5.3:* Mansell/Time inc/Katz; *Figure 5.5:* By permission of The Masters & Fellows of St. Johns College, Cambridge; *Figure 6.3:* Courtesy of the Archives, California Institute of Technology; *Figure 9.1:* Reprinted from *The New Solar System*, Third edition, © Sky Publishing, 1990; *Figure 11.9:* Courtesy of NOAO.

Title page picture

NASA Goddard Space Flight Center/COBE Science working group.

Index

Entries and page numbers in **bold type** refer to key words which are printed in **bold** in the text and which are defined in the Glossary. These are terms that we expect you to be able to explain the meaning of, and use correctly, both during and at the end of the course. An entry followed by ^{G} indicates a term which is defined in the Glossary but which is not bold in the text. Where the page number is given in *italics*, the indexed information is carried mainly or wholly in an illustration or table. Section summaries and answers to questions are not indexed.